THE ULTIMATE
MILWAUKEE BREWERS
TRIVIA BOOK

A Collection of Amazing Trivia Quizzes and Fun Facts for Die-Hard Brewers Fans!

Ray Walker

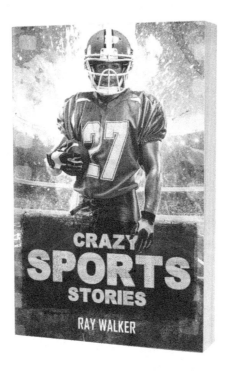

CONTENTS

INTRODUCTION

The Milwaukee Brewers were established in 1969. They have previously been known as the Seattle Pilots. No matter their name or location, they have consistently proven themselves to be a team who fights hard and is a force to be reckoned within the MLB.

Although the Brewers have not yet won the coveted World Series championship, they have won an American League pennant, two NL Central division titles, two AL East division titles and earned three Wild Card berths. They are very often a threat in the National League Central Division. They made their most recent, and only World Series appearance in 1982 against the St. Louis Cardinals.

The Milwaukee Brewers currently call American Family Field home, which opened in 2001. They play in one of the most difficult divisions in baseball, the National League Central, alongside the St. Louis Cardinals, Cincinnati Reds, Chicago Cubs, and Pittsburgh Pirates.

The thing about baseball is that it is a lot like life. There are good times and bad times, good days and bad days, but you have to do your absolute best to never give up. The Milwaukee

Brewers have proven that they refuse to give up and that they will do anything they need to do in order to bring a championship to the state of Wisconsin.

Winning is more than possible when you have a storied past like the Brewers. They have so much captivating history and so many undeniable player legacies to be profoundly proud of. Especially when you consider the players honored by Milwaukee with retired the uniform numbers: Bud Selig, Paul Molitor, Robin Yount, Rollie Fingers, Hank Aaron, plus the league-wide retirement of Jackie Robinson's number 42.

With such a storied team past that goes back generations, you're probably already very knowledgeable as the die-hard Brew Crew fan that you are. But keep in mind that all the stats in this book are current to the end of the 2020 season. So, let's test that knowledge to see if you truly are the world's biggest Brewers fan.

CHAPTER 1:

ORIGINS & HISTORY

QUIZ TIME!

1. Which of the following team names did the Milwaukee Brewers franchise once go by?

   a. Milwaukee Pilots

   b. Milwaukee Packers

   c. Seattle Pilots

   d. They have always been the Milwaukee Brewers.

2. In what year was the Milwaukee Brewers franchise established?

   a. 1869

   b. 1899

   c. 1949

   d. 1969

3. The Milwaukee Brewers' current home stadium is American Family Field.

   a. True

   b. False

4. Which division do the Milwaukee Brewers play in currently?

    a. American League East
    b. American League Central
    c. National League Central
    d. National League East

5. The Milwaukee Brewers have never earned a Wild Card berth.

    a. True
    b. False

6. How many National League pennants have the Milwaukee Brewers franchise won?

    a. 0
    b. 1
    c. 2
    d. 3

7. Who is the current principal owner of the Milwaukee Brewers?

    a. Larry Dolan
    b. Robert Nutting
    c. Mark Attanasio
    d. Arturo Moreno

8. Who is the winningest manager in Milwaukee Brewers history?

    a. Ned Yost
    b. Phil Garner

c. Dale Sveum

d. Del Crandall

9. What is the name of the Milwaukee Brewers' Triple-A team, and where are they located?

a. Indianapolis Indians

b. Jacksonville Jumbo Shrimp

c. Toledo Mud Hens

d. Nashville Sounds

10. Who was the first manager of the Milwaukee Brewers?

a. Alex Grammas

b. Dave Bristol

c. Joe Schultz

d. Roy McMillan

11. The Milwaukee Brewers have been members of all three American League divisions.

a. True

b. False

12. What is the name of the Milwaukee Brewers' current Spring Training home stadium?

a. Goodyear Ballpark

b. American Family Fields of Phoenix

c. Hohokam Stadium

d. Sloan Park

13. How many appearances have the Milwaukee Brewers made in the MLB playoffs?

a. 5

b. 7

c. 9

d. 11

14. How many World Series titles have the Milwaukee Brewers won?

    a. 0

    b. 1

    c. 2

    d. 3

15. The Milwaukee Brewers' current manager is Craig Counsell.

    a. True

    b. False

16. Which stadium was the first home of the Milwaukee Brewers?

    a. Milwaukee County Stadium

    b. American Family Fields

    c. Miller Park

    d. Sick's Stadium

17. Who is the current general manager of the Milwaukee Brewers?

    a. Mike Rizzo

    b. Matt Arnold

    c. David Forst

    d. Thad Levine

18. How many National League Central division titles have the Milwaukee Brewers won?

    a. 0
    b. 1
    c. 2
    d. 3

19. The Milwaukee Brewers won one pennant as a member of the American League.

    a. True
    b. False

20. David Stearns is the current president of the Milwaukee Brewers.

    a. True
    b. False

QUIZ ANSWERS

1. C – Seattle Pilots

2. D – 1969

3. A – True

4. C – National League Central

5. B – False (They won three, in 2008, 2019, and 2020.)

6. A – 0

7. C – Mark Attanasio

8. B – Phil Garner

9. D – Nashville Sounds

10. C – Joe Schultz

11. A – True (AL West 1969-71, AL East 1972-93, AL Central 1994-97)

12. B – American Family Fields of Phoenix

13. B – 7

14. A – 0

15. A – True

16. D – Sick's Stadium

17. B – Matt Arnold

18. C – 2

19. A – True (They won in 1982.)

20. A – True

DID YOU KNOW?

1. The Milwaukee Brewers franchise has had 19 managers so far in their history. They are: Joe Schultz, Dave Bristol, Roy McMillan, Del Crandall, Harvey Kuenn, Alex Grammas, George Bamberger, Buck Rodgers, Rene Lachemann, Tom Trebelhorn, Phil Garner, Jim Lefebvre, Davey Lopes, Jerry Royster, Ned Yost, Dale Sveum, Ken Macha, Ron Roenicke, and Craig Counsell.

2. The Milwaukee Brewers' current manager is Craig Counsell, and he has held the position since May 2015. He was an infielder in the MLB for 16 seasons, known for his unique batting stance. He was named the NLCS MVP in 2001.

3. Phil Garner is Milwaukee's all-time winningest manager with a record of 563-617, a .477 winning percentage. Garner managed the Brewers from 1992 to 1999.

4. Mark Attanasio is the current principal owner of the Milwaukee Brewers. He is the founder of Crescent Capital Group and part owner of the Milwaukee Admirals of the American Hockey League. Attanasio is a major sponsor of the Andy Warhol exhibit at the Milwaukee Art Museum. His brother Paul is a TV writer.

5. Milwaukee has hosted two All-Star Games so far in their history: in 1975 at County Stadium and in 2002 at Miller Park.

6. One pitcher for the Milwaukee Brewers has thrown a no-hitter in franchise history. It was thrown by Juan Nieves on April 15, 1987, against the Baltimore Orioles.

7. The Milwaukee Brewers won consecutive Wild Card berths in 2019 and 2020.

8. The Milwaukee Brewers' Double-A team is the Biloxi Shuckers. The franchise's High-A team is the Wisconsin Timber Rattlers, and the Low-A team is the Carolina Mudcats.

9. The Milwaukee Brewers' current mascot is named "Bernie Brewer." You can often find him going down the yellow slide at American Family Field after Brewers home runs.

10. The Milwaukee Brewers have retired five numbers so far in franchise history, six if you include Jackie Robinson's number 42, which is retired league-wide. The latest number to be retired is number 1 in honor of former Milwaukee Brewers owner and former MLB commissioner Bud Selig in 2015.

CHAPTER 2:

JERSEYS & NUMBERS

QUIZ TIME!

1. When the Brewers moved to Milwaukee, they did not have enough time to order new uniforms, so they wore Seattle Pilots uniforms and sewed the word "Brewers" on the front.

   a. True
   b. False

2. What are the Milwaukee Brewers' official team colors?

   a. Navy blue, yellow, and white
   b. Navy blue, royal blue, and yellow
   c. Royal blue, yellow, and white
   d. Navy blue, royal blue, and gold

3. The Milwaukee Brewers switched from pullover jerseys to button-down jerseys in 1990, making them the last American League team to do so.

   a. True
   b. False

4. Which of the following numbers is NOT retired by the Milwaukee Brewers?

    a. 4

    b. 19

    c. 34

    d. 48

5. What uniform number does Christian Yelich currently wear as a member of the Brewers?

    a. 2

    b. 21

    c. 22

    d. 27

6. What uniform number did Robin Yount wear during his time with the Milwaukee Brewers?

    a. 9

    b. 19

    c. 29

    d. 39

7. Teddy Higuera wore the uniform numbers 55 and 49 during his time with the Brewers.

    a. True

    b. False

8. Only one Milwaukee player has ever worn the uniform number 0 in franchise history. Who is that player?

    a. Curt Leskanic

    b. Jeffrey Leonard

c. Franklin Stubbs

d. Jose Cardenal

9. Who is the only Brewers player to have ever worn uniform number 67?

a. Josh Hader

b. Francisco Rodriguez

c. Mike Fiers

d. Jim Slaton

10. No Milwaukee Brewers player has ever won the uniform number 00.

a. True

b. False

11. What uniform number did Paul Molitor wear as a member of the Brewers?

a. 4

b. 14

c. 24

d. 34

12. What uniform number did Cecil Cooper wear as a member of the Milwaukee Brewers?

a. 5

b. 15

c. 17

d. 51

13. Ryan Braun wore the uniform number 8 during his time with the Brewers.

a. True

b. False

14. What uniform number did Don Money wear as a member of the Milwaukee Brewers?

    a. 3

    b. 7

    c. 9

    d. Both B and C

15. What uniform number did Prince Fielder wear as a member of the Brewers?

    a. 8

    b. 28

    c. 84

    d. All of the above

16. What uniform number did Hank Aaron wear as a member of the Milwaukee Brewers?

    a. 14

    b. 24

    c. 33

    d. 44

17. During his time with the Brewers, Rollie Fingers wore which uniform number?

    a. 14

    b. 24

    c. 34

    d. 44

18. What uniform number did Yovani Gallardo wear with the Milwaukee Brewers?

    a. 19

    b. 29

    c. 39

    d. 49

19. What uniform number did Geoff Jenkins wear as a member of the Brewers?

    a. 5

    b. 10

    c. 15

    d. All of the above

20. Jeff Cirillo wore the uniform numbers 6 and 26 during his time with the Milwaukee Brewers.

    a. True

    b. False

QUIZ ANSWERS

1. A – True

2. B – Navy blue, royal blue, and yellow

3. A – True

4. D – 48

5. C – 22

6. B – 19

7. A – True

8. C – Franklin Stubbs

9. D – Jim Slaton

10. B – False (Jeffrey Leonard and Curt Leskanic have worn uniform number 00.)

11. A – 4

12. B – 15

13. A – True

14. B – 7

15. B – 28

16. D – 44

17. C – 34

18. D – 49

19. A – 5

20. A – True

DID YOU KNOW?

1. The Milwaukee Brewers have retired six uniform numbers so far in franchise history: Bud Selig (number 1), Paul Molitor (number 4), Robin Yount (number 19), Rollie Fingers (number 34), Hank Aaron (number 44), and Jackie Robinson (number 42).

2. During his time with the Brewers, Jim Gantner wore the uniform numbers 11, 17, and 31.

3. Ben Oglivie wore the uniform number 24 during his time in Milwaukee.

4. During his time with the Brewers, Sixto Lezcano wore the uniform numbers 11, 16, and 37.

5. During his time in Milwaukee, Carlos Gomez wore the uniform number 27.

6. During his time with the Brewers, Chris Bosio wore the uniform number 29.

7. Jackie Robinson's number 42 is retired by the Milwaukee Brewers as well as the MLB as a whole. No Brewers or MLB player will ever wear number 42 again. The Yankees' Mariano Rivera was the final player to wear it.

8. During his time in Milwaukee, Gorman Thomas wore the uniform numbers 3, 20, and 44.

9. During his time with the Brewers, Bill Wegman wore the uniform number 46.

10. Jackie Bradley Jr. currently wears the uniform number 41 with the Milwaukee Brewers.

CHAPTER 3:

THE KID

QUIZ TIME!

1. How old was Robin Yount during his MLB debut?

    a. 18

    b. 19

    c. 20

    d. 21

2. Robin Yount played his entire 20-season MLB career with the Milwaukee Brewers.

    a. True

    b. False

    c. Where was Robin Yount born?

    d. Danville, California

    e. Woodland Hills, California

    f. Oswego, Illinois

    g. Danville, Illinois

3. When was Robin Yount born?

    a. May 16, 1955

    b. May 16, 1965

c. September 16, 1955

d. September 16, 1965

4. Robin Yount did NOT win a World Series championship during his time in the MLB.

   a. True

   b. False

5. How many All-Star Games was Robin Yount named to during his MLB career?

   a. 1

   b. 3

   c. 6

   d. 10

6. What year was Robin Yount inducted into the National Baseball Hall of Fame?

   a. 1995

   b. 1997

   c. 1999

   d. 2000

7. Robin Yount's brother, Larry, appeared in one MLB game for the Houston Astros.

   a. True

   b. False

8. What was Robin Yount's career batting average?

   a. .280

   b. .285

c. .295

d. .301

9. How many times was Robin Yount named AL MVP during his MLB career?

    a. 0

    b. 1

    c. 2

    d. 3

10. How many Gold Glove Awards did Robin Yount win during his MLB career?

    a. 0

    b. 1

    c. 2

    d. 3

11. Robin Yount was named the 1982 Major League Player of the Year.

    a. True

    b. False

12. How many Silver Slugger Awards did Robin Yount win during his MLB career?

    a. 1

    b. 2

    c. 3

    d. 4

13. Robin Yount's uniform number 19 was retired by the Milwaukee Brewers on May 29, 1994.

a. True

b. False

14. How many home runs did Robin Yount hit during his MLB career?

   a. 221

   b. 231

   c. 241

   d. 251

15. How many stolen bases did Robin Yount record during his MLB career?

   a. 171

   b. 191

   c. 271

   d. 291

16. Robin Yount's career wins above replacement (WAR) value is 77.3.

   a. True

   b. False

17. Over the course of his MLB career, how many times was Robin Yount named the AL Player of the Month?

   a. 1

   b. 2

   c. 3

   d. 4

18. How many hits did Robin Yount record during his MLB career?

    a. 1,542

    b. 2,142

    c. 2,542

    d. 3,142

19. Robin Yount is the only player in Milwaukee Brewers history to record 3,000 hits with the franchise.

    a. True

    b. False

QUIZ ANSWERS

1. A – 18

2. A – True

3. D – Danville, Illinois

4. C – September 16, 1955

5. A – True

6. B – 3

7. C – 1999

8. A – True

9. B – .285

10. C – 2 (He was given this honor in 1982 and 1989.)

11. B – 1

12. A – True

13. C – 3

14. A – True

15. D – 251

16. C – 271

17. A – True

18. C – 3 (He was named Player of the Month in April 1975, July 1982, and July 1989.)

19. D – 3,142

20. A – True

DID YOU KNOW?

1. Robin Yount married his high school sweetheart, Michele, in 1979.

2. There is a statue of Robin Yount at American Family Fields.

3. Robin Yount is a member of the Milwaukee Brewers Wall of Honor.

4. Between 2002 and 2004, Robin Yount was first base coach and bench coach for the Arizona Diamondbacks.

5. Alongside Hank Aaron, Paul Molitor, and Warren Spahn, Robin Yount threw out the ceremonial first pitch at the 2002 MLB All-Star Game held in Milwaukee.

6. Robin Yount holds the Brewers' all-time franchise records in games played, runs, doubles, plate appearances, at-bats, RBIs, triples, and walks.

7. Robin Yount was inducted into the National Baseball Hall of Fame on his first ballot in 1999 with 77.5% of the vote.

8. In 2014, Robin Yount won the Lombardi Award of Excellence from the Vince Lombardi Cancer Foundation.

9. In 2008, Robin Yount created a lemonade drink for charity called "Robinade."

10. Since 2012, Robin Yount has been a minority owner of the Lakeshore Chinooks, who are members of a NCAA college summer league called the Northwoods League.

CHAPTER 4:

CATCHY NICKNAMES

QUIZ TIME!

1. What nickname does Robin Yount go by?

   a. "The Dude"

   b. "The Man"

   c. "The Kid"

   d. "The Boy"

2. Ryan Braun goes by the nicknames "Hebrew Hammer" and "Ocho."

   a. True

   b. False

3. What nickname does Paul Molitor go by?

   a. "The Kickoff"

   b. "The Starter"

   c. "The Mover"

   d. "The Ignitor"

4. What nickname does Don Money go by?

a. "Big Money"

b. "Brooks"

c. "Big Donny"

d. "Looks"

5. What nickname does Jim Gantner go by?

   a. "Garfield"

   b. "Homer"

   c. "Gumby"

   d. "Mickey"

6. Which nickname did George Scott go by?

   a. "Crusher"

   b. "Hammer"

   c. "Smacker"

   d. "Boomer"

7. Carlos Gomez goes by the nicknames "Go-Go," "Cargo," and "El Titere."

   a. True

   b. False

8. What nickname does Gorman Thomas go by?

   a. "Big T"

   b. "G Tommy"

   c. "Stormin' Gorman"

   d. "Grillin' Gorman"

9. What nickname does Yovani Gallardo go by?

   a. "Do"

   b. "Yo"

c. "Vani"

d. "Yo-Ga"

10. What nickname does Prince Fielder go by?

    a. "Big Field"

    b. "Big Prince"

    c. "Uncle Prince"

    d. "Uncle Phil"

11. "Moose" is a nickname. What is Moose Haas's given first name?

    a. Zachary

    b. Keith

    c. Bryan

    d. Eugene

12. Christian Yelich goes by the nickname "Yeli."

    a. True

    b. False

13. Which nickname does Lorenzo Cain go by?

    a. "CrunchWrap"

    b. "LoCain"

    c. "Renny"

    d. Both A and B

14. What nickname does Travis Shaw go by?

    a. "Mayor of Ding Dong City"

    b. "The Mayor"

    c. "The Shaw-man"

    d. Both B and C

15. Khris Davis goes by the nickname "Khrush."

    a. True
    b. False

16. What nickname does Jim Edmonds go by?

    a. "J-Ed"
    b. "Eddie Baseball"
    c. "Jimmy Baseball"
    d. "Eddie"

17. Gary Sheffield goes by the nickname "Sheff."

    a. True
    b. False

18. "J.J" is a nickname. What is J.J. Hardy's full name?

    a. Jerry James Hardy
    b. James Jerry Hardy
    c. Jacob Jason Hardy
    d. Jason Jacob Hardy

19. What nickname does Craig Counsell go by?

    a. "Sheep"
    b. "Pig"
    c. "Cow"
    d. "Chicken"

20. Don Sutton goes by the nicknames "Black & Decker" and "The Mechanic."

    a. True
    b. False

QUIZ ANSWERS

1. C – "The Kid"

2. A – True

3. D – "The Ignitor"

4. B – "Brooks"

5. C – "Gumby"

6. D – "Boomer"

7. A – True

8. C – "Stormin' Gorman"

9. B – "Yo"

10. D – "Uncle Phil"

11. C – Bryan

12. A – True

13. D – Both A and B

14. A – "Mayor of Ding Dong City"

15. A – True

16. C – "Jimmy Baseball"

17. A – True

18. B – James Jerry Hardy

19. D – "Chicken"

20. A – True

DID YOU KNOW?

1. Alcides Escobar goes by the nickname "Esky."

2. Sal Bando went by the nickname "Captain Sal."

3. Rick Manning went by the nickname "Archie."

4. Matt Garza went by the nickname "The Count."

5. Scott Podsednik went by the nickname "The Podfather."

6. Mike Moustakas goes by the nickname "Moose."

7. Nelson Cruz goes by the nickname "Boomstick."

8. Eric Sogard goes by the nickname "Nerd Power."

9. "Rollie" is a nickname. Rollie Fingers's full name is Roland Glen Fingers.

10. Jackie Bradley Jr. goes by the simple nickname "JBJ."

CHAPTER 5:

THE IGNITOR

QUIZ TIME!

1. What is Paul Molitor's full name?

    a. Liam Paul Molitor

    b. Paul Liam Molitor

    c. Paul Leo Molitor

    d. Leo Paul Molitor

2. Paul Molitor played his entire 21-season MLB career with the Milwaukee Brewers.

    a. True

    b. False

3. Where was Paul Molitor born?

    a. Branson, Missouri

    b. Milwaukee, Wisconsin

    c. Toronto, Canada

    d. St. Paul, Minnesota

4. When was Paul Molitor born?

a. April 22, 1956

b. April 22, 1966

c. August 22, 1956

d. August 22, 1966

5. Paul Molitor did NOT win a World Series championship during his MLB career.

a. True

b. False

6. How many All-Star Games was Paul Molitor named to during his MLB career?

a. 5

b. 7

c. 9

d. 11

7. How many Silver Slugger Awards did Paul Molitor win during his MLB career?

a. 1

b. 2

c. 3

d. 4

8. Paul Molitor was named the 1993 World Series MVP.

a. True

b. False

9. Paul Molitor was manager of which MLB team from 2015 to 2018?

a. Milwaukee Brewers

b. Washington Nationals

c. Toronto Blue Jays

d. Minnesota Twins

10. What year was Paul Molitor named the AL Manager of the Year?

a. 2015

b. 2016

c. 2017

d. 2018

11. What year was Paul Molitor inducted into the National Baseball Hall of Fame?

a. 2004

b. 2007

c. 2010

d. 2014

12. Paul Molitor was inducted into the Wisconsin Athletic Hall of Fame in 1999.

a. True

b. False

13. What year did the Milwaukee Brewers retire Paul Molitor's uniform number 4?

a. 1998

b. 1999

c. 2001

d. 2004

14. Paul Molitor was the Seattle Mariners' hitting coach for the 2004 season.

    a. True
    b. False

15. How many home runs did Paul Molitor hit during his MLB career?

    a. 123
    b. 203
    c. 234
    d. 303

16. How many at-bats did Paul Molitor collect during his MLB career?

    a. 7,835
    b. 8,835
    c. 9,835
    d. 10,835

17. Paul Molitor's career batting average is .306.

    a. True
    b. False

18. How many hits did Paul Molitor collect during his MLB career?

    a. 3,019
    b. 3,119
    c. 3,219
    d. 3,319

19. How many stolen bases did Paul Molitor collect during his MLB career?

   a. 304
   b. 404
   c. 504
   d. 604

20. Paul Molitor collected 1,307 RBIs during his MLB career.

   a. True
   b. False

QUIZ ANSWERS

1. C – Paul Leo Molitor

2. B – False (He played for the Milwaukee Brewers, Toronto Blue Jays, and Minnesota Twins.)

3. D – St. Paul, Minnesota

4. C – August 22, 1956

5. B – False (He won a World Series in 1993.)

6. B – 7

7. D – 4

8. A – True

9. D – Minnesota Twins

10. C – 2017

11. A – 2004

12. A – True

13. B – 1999

14. A – True

15. C – 234

16. D – 10,385

17. A – True

18. D – 3,319

19. C – 504

20. A – True

DID YOU KNOW?

1. Paul Molitor was 21 years old during his MLB debut. He was 42 years old during his final game played in the MLB.

2. In 1978, Paul Molitor came in second place for the American League Rookie of the Year Award. The winner was Lou Whitaker of the Detroit Tigers.

3. Paul Molitor was named the AL Player of the Month twice in his MLB career, and he was named the AL Player of the Week five times in his career.

4. Paul Molitor's career WAR value is 75.7.

5. Paul Molitor attended college at the University of Minnesota.

6. In his early career, Paul Molitor used marijuana and cocaine. He has since lectured at schools about the dangers of using drugs.

7. Between his sophomore and junior seasons at Minnesota, Paul Molitor suffered a broken jaw. It was wired shut for eight weeks.

8. Paul Molitor is a member of the Milwaukee Brewers Wall of Honor and the American Family Field Walk of Fame.

9. Paul Molitor wore uniform number 4 with the Milwaukee Brewers and Minnesota Twins. He wore number 19 during his time with the Toronto Blue Jays.

10. Paul Molitor was named to the Major League Baseball All-Time Team, which was chosen in 1997. He was chosen as the All-Time Team's designated hitter. Other members of the MLB All-Time Team include: Johnny Bench, Lou Gehrig, Rogers Hornsby, Honus Wagner, Mike Schmidt, Ted Williams, Willie Mays, Babe Ruth, Walter Johnson, Sandy Koufax, Dennis Eckersley, and Casey Stengel.

CHAPTER 6:

STATISTICALLY SPEAKING

QUIZ TIME!

1. Ryan Braun currently holds the Milwaukee Brewers franchise record for the most home runs. How many home runs did he hit during his MLB career?

    a. 342

    b. 352

    c. 362

    d. 372

2. Pitcher Jim Slaton has the most wins in Milwaukee Brewers franchise history, with 117.

    a. True

    b. False

3. Which pitcher holds the Milwaukee Brewers' record for most career shutouts thrown, with 19?

    a. Bill Travers

    b. Teddy Higuera

    c. Mike Caldwell

    d. Jim Slaton

4. Which Milwaukee Brewers batter currently holds the single-season record for strikeouts, with 206?

   a. Rob Deer

   b. Rickie Weeks

   c. Chris Carter

   d. Jose Hernandez

5. Yovani Gallardo has the most strikeouts in Milwaukee Brewers franchise history with how many?

   a. 1,006

   b. 1,116

   c. 1,226

   d. 1,336

6. Who has the most stolen bases in Milwaukee Brewers franchise history, with 412?

   a. Carlos Gomez

   b. Ryan Braun

   c. Robin Yount

   d. Paul Molitor

7. Dan Plesac holds the record for most saves in Milwaukee Brewers history, with 133.

   a. True

   b. False

8. Who holds the Milwaukee Brewers record for being intentionally walked, with 115?

   a. Cecil Cooper

   b. Robin Yount

c. Prince Fielder

d. Paul Molitor

9. Which player holds the Milwaukee franchise record for home runs in a single season, with 50?

a. Ryan Braun

b. Prince Fielder

c. Richie Sexson

d. Christian Yelich

10. Which batter holds the single-season Milwaukee Brewers record for hits, with 219?

a. Robin Yount

b. Paul Molitor

c. Cecil Cooper

d. Jeff Cirillo

11. Which two players are tied for the single-season Milwaukee Brewers record for double plays grounded into, with 26 each?

a. Jeff Cirillo and George Scott

b. Royce Clayton and George Scott

c. Royce Clayton and Jeff Cirillo

d. Ted Simmons and George Scott

12. Robin Yount holds the record for the most sacrifice flies in Milwaukee Brewers all-time franchise history, with 123.

a. True

b. False

13. Jim Slaton threw the most wild pitches in Milwaukee Brewers franchise history with how many?

    a. 61

    b. 71

    c. 81

    d. 91

14. Paul Molitor holds the Milwaukee Brewers single-season record for most triples. How many did he hit in 1979?

    a. 6

    b. 10

    c. 16

    d. 20

15. Which hitter has the most walks in Milwaukee Brewers franchise history, with 966?

    a. Ryan Braun

    b. Prince Fielder

    c. Paul Molitor

    d. Robin Yount

16. Which Brewers hitter holds the all-time franchise record for best overall batting average at .309?

    a. Darryl Hamilton

    b. Jeff Cirillo

    c. Christian Yelich

    d. Fernando Vina

17. Robin Yount holds the Milwaukee Brewers' record for most runs scored, with 1,632.

a. True

b. False

18. Robin Yount has the most plate appearances all time in Brewers franchise history with how many?

a. 9,249

b. 10,249

c. 11,249

d. 12,249

19. Which pitcher holds the Milwaukee franchise record for most saves in a single season, with 46?

a. Francisco Cordero

b. John Axford

c. Dan Plesac

d. Trevor Hoffman

20. Jim Slaton holds the Brewers franchise record for most losses, with 121.

a. True

b. False

QUIZ ANSWERS

1. B – 352

2. A – True

3. D – Jim Slaton

4. C – Chris Carter (2016)

5. C – 1,226

6. D – Paul Molitor

7. A – True

8. C – Prince Fielder

9. B – Prince Fielder (2007)

10. C – Cecil Cooper (1980)

11. A – Jeff Cirillo (1998) and George Scott (1975)

12. A – True

13. B – 71

14. C – 16

15. D – Robin Yount

16. C – Christian Yelich

17. A – True

18. D – 12,249

19. B – John Axford (2011)

20. A – True

DID YOU KNOW?

1. Jim Slaton threw the most innings in Milwaukee Brewers franchise history, with 2,025.3 total. Coming in second is Mike Caldwell who threw 1,604.6 innings total.

2. Paul Molitor had the best single-season batting average in Milwaukee Brewers franchise history at .353 in 1987. Coming in second is Cecil Cooper whose batting average was .352 in 1980.

3. Scott Podsednik holds the Milwaukee Brewers franchise record for stolen base percentage, with 83.09% accuracy. However, Paul Molitor holds the franchise records for stolen bases, with 412, and the most times caught stealing at 115.

4. Robin Yount has the most extra base hits in Milwaukee Brewers franchise history, with 960. Second on the list is Ryan Braun with 809.

5. Christian Yelich holds the Milwaukee franchise record for at-bats per home run at 14.1. Essentially, what this means is that, on average, Yelich hits a home run about every 14 at-bats.

6. Yovani Gallardo holds the Milwaukee Brewers franchise record for strikeouts per nine innings pitched at 8.558. Essentially, what this means is that, during his time with the Brewers, Gallardo recorded about eight or nine strikeouts in every nine innings that he pitched.

7. Rickie Weeks holds the Milwaukee Brewers' record for the most hit by pitches, with 125. On the other hand, Dave Bush holds the franchise record for most batters hit, with 58.

8. Robin Yount holds the Milwaukee Brewers franchise record for career doubles hit, with 583. Second on the list is Ryan Braun with 408.

9. Mike Caldwell holds the Brewers' single-season record for wins with 22 in 1978. On the other hand, Clyde Wright holds the franchise single-season record for most losses with 20 in 1974.

10. Ben Sheets holds the Milwaukee Brewers franchise record for most strikeouts in a single season with 264 in 2004.

CHAPTER 7:
THE TRADE MARKET

QUIZ TIME!

1. On December 12, 1980, the Milwaukee Brewers traded Sixto Lezcano, Lary Sorensen, Dave LaPoint, and David Green to which team for Rollie Fingers, Ted Simmons, and Pete Vuckovich?

   a. San Diego Padres
   b. St. Louis Cardinals
   c. Oakland A's
   d. Chicago White Sox

2. On January 25, 2018, Milwaukee traded Lewis Brinson, Monte Harrison, Isan Diaz, and Jordan Yamamoto to which team for Christian Yelich?

   a. Los Angeles Dodgers
   b. Tampa Bay Rays
   c. New York Mets
   d. Miami Marlins

3. The Milwaukee Brewers have made six trades with the Arizona Diamondbacks all time.

   a. True

   b. False

4. On July 7, 2008, the Brewers traded Matt LaPorta, Rob Bryson, Zach Jackson, and a player to be named later (Michael Brantley) to which team for C.C. Sabathia?

   a. Pittsburgh Pirates

   b. Houston Astros

   c. Cleveland Indians

   d. New York Yankees

5. The Milwaukee Brewers have made eight trades with the Colorado Rockies all time.

   a. True

   b. False

6. On December 6, 1976, Milwaukee traded George Scott and Bernie Carbo to which team for Cecil Cooper?

   a. Kansas City Royals

   b. Boston Red Sox

   c. New York Yankees

   d. Cincinnati Reds

7. On August 30, 1982, the Brewers traded several players to be named later (Kevin Bass, Frank DiPino, and Mike Madden) and cash to which team for Don Sutton?

   a. Houston Astros

   b. Los Angeles Dodgers

c. California Angels

d. Oakland A's

8. On October 10, 1971, Milwaukee traded Tommy Harper, Lew Krausse, Marty Pattin, and Patrick Skrable to which team for George Scott, Jim Lonborg, Ken Brett, Billy Conigliaro, Joe Lahoud, and Don Pavletich?

a. New York Yankees

b. Philadelphia Phillies

c. Kansas City Royals

d. Boston Red Sox

9. On July 30, 2015, Milwaukee traded Carlos Gomez and Mike Fiers to which team for Josh Hader, Adrian Houser, Brett Phillips, and Domingo Santana?

a. Texas Rangers

b. Minnesota Twins

c. Houston Astros

d. Oakland A's

10. The Milwaukee Brewers have made eight trades with the Miami Marlins all time.

a. True

b. False

11. On October 31, 1972, the Brewers traded Ken Brett, Earl Stephenson, Jim Lonborg, and Ken Sanders to which team for Don Money, John Vukovich, and Bill Champion.

a. Cincinnati Reds

b. Baltimore Orioles

c. Boston Red Sox

d. Philadelphia Phillies

12. The Milwaukee Brewers have made 12 trades with the Seattle Mariners all time.

   a. True

   b. False

13. How many trades have the Brewers made with the Pittsburgh Pirates all time?

   a. 12

   b. 15

   c. 20

   d. 22

14. The Milwaukee Brewers have made 13 trades with the San Diego Padres all time.

   a. True

   b. False

15. On December 19, 2010, Milwaukee traded Lorenzo Cain, Alcides Escobar, Jeremy Jeffress, and Jake Odorizzi to the Kansas City Royals for which player, along with Yuniesky Betancourt?

   a. John Axford

   b. Zack Greinke

   c. Yovani Gallardo

   d. LaTroy Hawkins

16. On December 9, 1977, the Brewers traded Jim Slaton and Rich Folkers to which team for Ben Oglivie?

   a. Texas Rangers
   b. California Angels
   c. Boston Red Sox
   d. Detroit Tigers

17. On November 2, 1974, Milwaukee traded Dave May and a player to be named later (Roger Alexander) to the Atlanta Braves for which player?

   a. Sixto Lezcano
   b. George Scott
   c. Hank Aaron
   d. Don Money

18. On August 31, 1996, the Brewers traded Kevin Seitzer to which team for Jeromy Burnitz?

   a. New York Mets
   b. Cleveland Indians
   c. Colorado Rockies
   d. Los Angeles Dodgers

19. On June 15, 1977, Milwaukee traded Rick O'Keeffe and Garry Pyka to which team for Mike Caldwell?

   a. San Diego Padres
   b. San Francisco Giants
   c. Cincinnati Reds
   d. New York Mets

20. The Brewers have made nine trades with the Tampa Bay Rays all time.

    a. True
    b. False

QUIZ ANSWERS

1. B – St. Louis Cardinals

2. D – Miami Marlins

3. A – True

4. C – Cleveland Indians

5. A – True

6. B – Boston Red Sox

7. A – Houston Astros

8. D – Boston Red Sox

9. C – Houston Astros

10. A – True

11. D – Philadelphia Phillies

12. A – True

13. A – 12

14. A – True

15. B – Zack Greinke

16. D – Detroit Tigers

17. C – Hank Aaron

18. B – Cleveland Indians

19. C – Cincinnati Reds

20. A – True

DID YOU KNOW?

1. On June 6, 1983, the Brewers traded Gorman Thomas, Ernie Camacho, and Jamie Easterly to the Cleveland Indians for Rick Manning and Rick Waits.

2. On January 19, 2015, Milwaukee traded Yovani Gallardo and cash considerations to the Texas Rangers for Corey Knebel, Luis Sardinas, and Marcos Diplan.

3. On August 1, 2016, the Brewers traded Jonathan Lucroy and Jeremy Jeffress to the Texas Rangers for Lewis Brinson, Luis Ortiz, and a player to be named later (Ryan Cordell).

4. On March 30, 1986, Milwaukee traded Moose Haas to the Oakland A's for Mike Fulmer, Pete Kendrick, Steve Kiefer, and Charlie O'Brien.

5. On December 1, 2003, the Brewers traded Shane Nance, Richie Sexson, and a player to be named later (Noochie Varner) to the Arizona Diamondbacks for Craig Counsell, Chris Capuano, Lyle Overbay, Chad Moeller, Jorge De La Rosa, and Junior Spivey.

6. On December 6, 1976, Milwaukee traded Jim Colborn and Darrell Porter to the Kansas City Royals for Jamie Quirk, Jim Wohlford, and a player to be named later (Bob McClure).

7. On July 28, 2006, the Brewers traded Nelson Cruz and Carlos Lee to the Texas Rangers for Francisco Cordero, Julian Cordero, Kevin Mench, and Laynce Nix.

8. On May 21, 2009, Milwaukee traded Tony Gwynn Jr. to the San Diego Padres for Jody Gerut.

9. The Brewers have made 17 trades with the Los Angeles Angels.

10. The Milwaukee Brewers and Minnesota Twins have made 14 trades.

CHAPTER 8:

DRAFT DAY

QUIZ TIME!

1. With which pick in the 1st round of the 1973 MLB Draft did the Milwaukee Brewers select Robin Yount?

    a. 1st
    b. 2nd
    c. 3rd
    d. 4th

2. With which pick in the 1st round of the 1977 MLB Draft, did the Brewers select Paul Molitor?

    a. 1st
    b. 2nd
    c. 3rd
    d. 4th

3. With which pick in the 1st round of the 2005 MLB Draft, did Milwaukee select Ryan Braun?

    a. 1st
    b. 2nd

c. 3rd

d. 5th

4. Cecil Cooper was drafted by which team in the 6th round of the 1968 MLB Draft?

   a. Milwaukee Brewers

   b. Boston Red Sox

   c. Atlanta Braves

   d. St. Louis Cardinals

5. In which round of the 1991 MLB Draft, did the Milwaukee Brewers select Jeff Cirillo?

   a. 2nd

   b. 3rd

   c. 10th

   d. 11th

6. Jim Gantner was drafted by the Brewers in the 12th round of which year's MLB Draft?

   a. 1974

   b. 1975

   c. 1976

   d. 1977

7. Jason Kendall was drafted by the Pittsburgh Pirates in the 1st round, 23rd overall in the 1992 MLB Draft.

   a. True

   b. False

8. With which pick in the 1st round of the 1995 MLB Draft, did Milwaukee select Geoff Jenkins?

a. 5th

b. 9th

c. 11th

d. 19th

9. Ben Oglivie was drafted by which team in the 11th round of the 1968 MLB Draft?

    a. Milwaukee Brewers

    b. New York Yankees

    c. Detroit Tigers

    d. Boston Red Sox

10. Chris Bosio was drafted by the Milwaukee Brewers in the 2nd round of the 1982 MLB Draft.

    a. True

    b. False

11. Yovani Gallardo was drafted by the Brewers in which round of the 2004 MLB Draft?

    a. 2nd

    b. 3rd

    c. 5th

    d. 6th

12. Gorman Thomas was drafted by the Seattle Pilots in the 1st round (21st overall) of the 1969 MLB Draft.

    a. True

    b. False

13. Bill Wegman was drafted by Milwaukee in the 5th round of the which year's MLB Draft?

a. 1980

b. 1981

c. 1982

d. 1983

14. Mike Caldwell was drafted by which team in the 12th round of the 1971 MLB Draft?

    a. San Francisco Giants

    b. Cincinnati Reds

    c. San Diego Padres

    d. Milwaukee Brewers

15. Jonathan Lucroy was drafted by the Brewers in which round of the 2007 MLB Draft?

    a. 2nd

    b. 3rd

    c. 4th

    d. 5th

16. Jeromy Burnitz was drafted by which team in the 1st round (17th overall) of the 1990 MLB Draft?

    a. Cleveland Indians

    b. New York Mets

    c. Los Angeles Dodgers

    d. Colorado Rockies

17. With which pick in the 1st round of the 2002 MLB Draft, did the Brewers select Prince Fielder?

    a. 1st

    b. 2nd

c. 6th

d. 7th

18. Moose Haas was drafted by Milwaukee in which round of the 1974 MLB Draft?

a. 2nd

b. 3rd

c. 8th

d. 9th

19. When was Corey Hart drafted in the 11th round of the MLB Draft by the Brewers?

a. 1998

b. 1999

c. 2000

d. 2001

20. With the 23rd overall pick in the 1st round of the 2010 MLB Draft, the Florida Marlins selected Christian Yelich.

a. True

b. False

QUIZ ANSWERS

1. C – 3rd

2. C – 3rd

3. D – 5th

4. B – Boston Red Sox

5. D – 11th

6. A – 1974

7. A – True

8. B – 9th

9. D – Boston Red Sox

10. A – True

11. A – 2nd

12. A – True

13. B – 1981

14. C – San Diego Padres

15. B – 3rd

16. B – New York Mets

17. D – 7th

18. A – 2nd

19. C – 2000

20. A – True

DID YOU KNOW?

1. Lorenzo Cain was drafted by the Brewers in the 17th round of the 2004 MLB Draft.

2. Rickie Weeks was drafted by Milwaukee in the 1st round (2nd overall) of the 2003 MLB Draft.

3. Craig Counsell was drafted by the Colorado Rockies in the 11th round of the 1992 MLB Draft.

4. Chris Capuano was drafted in the 8th round of the 1999 MLB Draft by the Arizona Diamondbacks.

5. B.J. Surhoff was drafted by Milwaukee in the 1st round (1st overall) of the 1985 MLB Draft.

6. Darryl Hamilton was drafted in the 11th round of the 1986 MLB Draft by the Brewers.

7. Gary Sheffield was drafted by Milwaukee in the 1st round (6th overall) of the 1986 MLB Draft.

8. Dan Plesac was drafted in the 1st round (26th overall) of the 1983 MLB Draft by the Brewers.

9. Sal Bando was drafted by the Kansas City Athletics in the 6th round of the 1965 MLB Draft.

10. Mike Matheny was drafted in the 8th round of the 1991 MLB Draft by the Brewers.

CHAPTER 9:

ODDS & ENDS

QUIZ TIME!

1. Which former Brewer takes a nap as a pregame ritual?

    a. Jonathan Lucroy

    b. Ryan Braun

    c. Nelson Cruz

    d. Yovani Gallardo

2. Dale Sveum is the cousin of former Toronto Blue Jays player John Olreud.

    a. True

    b. False

3. When he was eight years old, former Brewer Prince Fielder starred in a commercial in which he struck out his father, Cecil, for which company?

    a. Chevrolet

    b. McDonald's

    c. Coca-Cola

    d. Disneyland

4. Former Brewer Dan Plesac has a nephew, Zach, who currently pitches for which team?

    a. Pittsburgh Pirates
    b. St. Louis Cardinals
    c. New York Mets
    d. Cleveland Indians

5. For 25 years, Dave Parker owned several franchises in Cincinnati for which fast food restaurant?

    a. McDonald's
    b. Popeye's Chicken
    c. Starbucks
    d. Dunkin' Donuts

6. Zack Greinke is a minority owner in a franchise of which fast food restaurant?

    a. In-N-Out
    b. Dunkin' Donuts
    c. Chipotle
    d. Ben & Jerry's

7. Former Brewer Dan Plesac is currently an analyst on MLB Network.

    a. True
    b. False

8. Jason Kendall wrote a book, *Throwback: A Big-League Catcher Tells How the Game Is Really Played*, which was released in May 2014.

a. True

b. False

9. In 2012, Ryan Braun opened up a restaurant called 8-Twelve in Brookfield, Wisconsin, with which NFL quarterback?

   a. Cam Newton

   b. Russell Wilson

   c. Aaron Rodgers

   d. Tom Brady

10. Jeff Cirillo is currently a scout for which MLB team?

    a. Colorado Rockies

    b. Los Angeles Angels

    c. Arizona Diamondbacks

    d. San Diego Padres

11. Ben Sheets won which medal at the 2000 Summer Olympics?

    a. Gold

    b. Silver

    c. Bronze

    d. None of the above

12. Prince Fielder was named after the musician Prince because his mother was a huge fan of the singer.

    a. True

    b. False

13. Jonathan Lucroy played for which team in the 2017 World Baseball Classic?

a. Canada

b. Netherlands

c. Italy

d. USA

14. Over the course of his 16-season MLB career, Kyle Lohse defeated all 30 MLB teams.

a. True

b. False

15. Which animated TV show did Sal Bando make a guest appearance on in 2006?

a. *Spongebob Squarepants*

b. *The Simpsons*

c. *Family Guy*

d. *Futurama*

16. Rickie Weeks's brother, Jemile, played in the MLB from 2011 to 2016.

a. True

b. False

17. Which cell phone company has Ned Yost done commercials for?

a. T-Mobile

b. AT&T

c. Sprint

d. Verizon

18. B.J. Surhoff's dad played two seasons in which other professional sports league?

a. NHL

b. MLS

c. NBA

d. NFL

19. Mike Matheny was manager of which team from 2012 to 2018?

a. St. Louis Cardinals

b. Kansas City Royals

c. Toronto Blue Jays

d. San Francisco Giants

20. Chris Capuano appeared on an episode of *The Young and the Restless* in 2007.

a. True

b. False

QUIZ ANSWERS

1. C – Nelson Cruz

2. A – True

3. B – McDonald's

4. D – Cleveland Indians

5. B – Popeye's Chicken

6. C – Chipotle

7. A – True

8. A – True

9. C – Aaron Rodgers

10. B – Los Angeles Angels

11. A – Gold

12. A – True

13. D – USA

14. A – True

15. B – *The Simpsons*

16. A – True

17. D – Verizon

18. C – NBA

19. A – St. Louis Cardinals

20. A – True

DID YOU KNOW?

1. C.C. Sabathia was born in Vallejo, California, and resided in Fairfield, California, close to where he was born and raised until he signed with the Yankees.

2. Carlos Lee currently owns and operates cattle ranches in Houston.

3. Teddy Higuera has served as the pitching coach for Team Mexico in the 2006, 2009, and 2013 World Baseball Classic.

4. Jim Gantner was inducted into the Wisconsin Athletic Hall of Fame in 2005. He is also a partial owner of the bar Scud's Buds in Eden.

5. Sixto Lezcano was the batting coach for the Danville Braves, who are a rookie league affiliate of the Atlanta Braves.

6. Chris Bosio currently offers pitching and hitting lessons in Phoenix, Arizona, for baseball players.

7. Stormin' Gorman's BBQ Sauce, created by Gorman Thomas, is available at American Family Field and some Wisconsin establishments.

8. Rollie Fingers is one of only 10 players in MLB history to have their uniform numbers retired by more than one MLB team.

9. In 2021, Corey Hart became the hitting coach for the Buffalo Bisons, the Toronto Blue Jays' Triple-A affiliate.

10. John Axford has a bachelor's degree in film and television from Notre Dame University.

CHAPTER 10:

OUTFIELDERS

QUIZ TIME!

1. How many All-Star Games was Corey Hart named to during his 11-season MLB career?

   a. 1

   b. 2

   c. 3

   d. 5

2. Gary Sheffield won five Silver Slugger Awards during his 22-season MLB career.

   a. True

   b. False

3. Ryan Braun was named the National League Rookie of the Year in which season?

   a. 2005

   b. 2006

   c. 2007

   d. 2008

4. Geoff Jenkins spent his entire 11-season career with the Milwaukee Brewers.

   a. True

   b. False

5. How many All-Star Games was Carlos Gomez named to during his 13-season MLB career?

   a. 1

   b. 2

   c. 3

   d. 4

6. How many Gold Glove Awards has Lorenzo Cain won?

   a. 1

   b. 2

   c. 3

   d. 4

7. Robin Yount played his entire 20-season MLB career with the Brewers.

   a. True

   b. False

8. Over the course of his 11-season MLB career, Scott Podsednik played for the Milwaukee Brewers, Seattle Mariners, Kansas City Royals, Colorado Rockies, Los Angeles Dodgers, Boston Red Sox, and which other franchise?

   a. Oakland A's

   b. St. Louis Cardinals

c. Tampa Bay Rays

d. Chicago White Sox

9. How many seasons did B.J. Surhoff spend with the Brewers?

    a. 7

    b. 8

    c. 9

    d. 10

10. How many All-Star Games was Carlos Lee named to during his 14-season MLB career?

    a. 1

    b. 2

    c. 3

    d. 4

11. How many All-Star Games was Dave Parker named to during his 19-season MLB career?

    a. 2

    b. 3

    c. 5

    d. 7

12. Hank Aaron spent only two seasons with Milwaukee.

    a. True

    b. False

13. How many Gold Glove Awards did Mike Cameron win during his 17-season MLB career?

a. 1

b. 3

c. 5

d. 6

14. Ben Oglivie spent nine seasons with the Milwaukee Brewers, three seasons with the Boston Red Sox, and four years with which other team?

a. New York Yankees

b. Texas Rangers

c. Detroit Tigers

d. Baltimore Orioles

15. How many Gold Glove Awards did Sixto Lezcano win during his 12-season MLB career?

a. 0

b. 1

c. 2

d. 3

16. How many seasons did Gorman Thomas spend with the Brewers?

a. 6

b. 8

c. 10

d. 11

17. How many All-Star Games was Jeromy Burnitz named to during his 14-season MLB career?

a. 1

b. 2

c. 4

d. 5

18. Rick Manning spent five seasons with the Milwaukee Brewers and nine seasons with which other franchise?

    a. San Francisco Giants

    b. San Diego Padres

    c. Cleveland Indians

    d. Houston Astros

19. How many seasons did Darryl Hamilton spend with Milwaukee?

    a. 4

    b. 5

    c. 6

    d. 7

20. Tony Gwynn Jr. spent three seasons of his MLB career with the Brewers.

    a. True

    b. False

QUIZ ANSWERS

1. B – 2

2. A – True

3. C – 2007

4. B – False (He played 10 seasons with the Brewers and one with the Philadelphia Phillies.)

5. B – 2

6. A – 1

7. A – True

8. D – Chicago White Sox

9. C – 9

10. C – 3

11. D – 7

12. A – True

13. B – 3

14. C – Detroit Tigers

15. B – 1

16. D – 11

17. A – 1

18. C – Cleveland Indians

19. D – 7

20. A – True

DID YOU KNOW?

1. Robin Yount spent his entire 20-season MLB career with the Milwaukee Brewers. He is a member of the National Baseball Hall of Fame, two-time MVP, three-time All-Star, Gold Glove Award winner, three-time Silver Slugger Award winner, and the 1982 Major League Player of the Year.

2. Hank Aaron spent two seasons of his MLB career with the Milwaukee Brewers. He also played for the Milwaukee/ Atlanta Braves. He is a member of the National Baseball Hall of Fame, the 1957 NL MVP, 25-time All-Star, World Series champion, three-time Gold Glove Award winner, and two-time batting champion.

3. Ryan Braun spent his entire 14-season MLB career with the Milwaukee Brewers. He was the 2011 NL MVP, 2007 NL Rookie of the Year, a six-time All-Star, and five-time Silver Slugger Award winner.

4. Geoff Jenkins spent 10 seasons of his MLB career with the Milwaukee Brewers. He also played for the Philadelphia Phillies. He was an All-Star in 2003 and won the 2008 World Series with the Phillies.

5. Ben Oglivie spent nine seasons of his MLB career with the Milwaukee Brewers. He also played for the Detroit Tigers and Boston Red Sox. He was a three-time All-Star and 1980 Silver Slugger Award winner.

6. Lorenzo Cain currently plays for the Milwaukee Brewers. He also played for the Kansas City Royals. He is a two-time All-Star, 2019 Gold Glove Award winner, World Series champion, and the 2014 ALCS MVP.

7. Gorman Thomas spent 11 seasons of his MLB career with the Milwaukee Brewers. He also played for the Seattle Mariners and Cleveland Indians. He was an All-Star in 1981.

8. Sixto Lezcano spent seven seasons of his MLB career with the Milwaukee Brewers. He also played for the San Diego Padres, Philadelphia Phillies, Pittsburgh Pirates, and St. Louis Cardinals. He won the Gold Glove Award in 1979.

9. B.J. Surhoff spent nine seasons of his MLB career with the Milwaukee Brewers. He also played for the Baltimore Orioles and Atlanta Braves. He was named an All-Star in 1999.

10. Dave Parker spent a single season of his MLB career with the Milwaukee Brewers. He also played for the Pittsburgh Pirates, Cincinnati Reds, Oakland A's, California Angels, and Toronto Blue Jays. He was the 1978 NL MVP, a seven-time All-Star, two-time World Series champion, three-time Gold Glove Award winner, three-time Silver Slugger Award winner, two-time batting champion, and the 1979 All-Star Game MVP.

CHAPTER 11:

INFIELDERS

QUIZ TIME!

1. How many Silver Slugger Awards did Paul Molitor win during his 21-season MLB career?

    a. 2

    b. 3

    c. 4

    d. 5

2. Cecil Cooper spent 11 seasons of his MLB career with the Milwaukee Brewers.

    a. True

    b. False

3. How many All-Star Games was Don Money named to during his 16-season MLB career?

    a. 2

    b. 4

    c. 6

    d. 8

4. How many All-Star Games was Jeff Cirillo named to during his 14-season MLB career?

    a. 0
    b. 1
    c. 2
    d. 3

5. How many Gold Glove Awards did George Scott win during his 14-season MLB career?

    a. 2
    b. 4
    c. 6
    d. 8

6. How many Silver Slugger Awards did Prince Fielder win during his 12-season MLB career?

    a. 1
    b. 2
    c. 3
    d. 4

7. Jim Gantner spent his entire 17-season MLB career with the Milwaukee Brewers.

    a. True
    b. False

8. How many seasons did Rickie Weeks spend with the Brewers?

    a. 8
    b. 9

c. 10

d. 11

9. How many seasons did current Brewers manager Craig Counsell spend with the franchise during his 16-season playing career?

a. 5

b. 6

c. 8

d. 9

10. How many Gold Glove Awards did J.J. Hardy win during his 13-season MLB career?

a. 1

b. 2

c. 3

d. 4

11. How many All-Star Games was Willie Randolph named to during his 18-season MLB career?

a. 2

b. 4

c. 6

d. 8

12. Pat Listach was named the 1992 American League Rookie of the Year.

a. True

b. False

13. John Jaha spent seven seasons with the Milwaukee Brewers and three seasons with which other team?

    a. New York Mets
    b. California Angels
    c. Chicago Cubs
    d. Oakland A's

14. Former Brewers manager Dale Sveum spent how many seasons of his playing career with Milwaukee?

    a. 3
    b. 4
    c. 5
    d. 7

15. How many All-Star Games was Sal Bando named to during his 16-season MLB career?

    a. 1
    b. 2
    c. 3
    d. 4

16. Jose Valentin was named the 1994 American League Rookie of the Year.

    a. True
    b. False

17. How many All-Star Games was Kevin Seitzer named to during his 12-season MLB career?

    a. 0
    b. 1

c. 2

d. 3

18. How many All-Star Games was Aramis Ramirez named to during his 18-season MLB career?

a. 2

b. 3

c. 4

d. 6

19. How many All-Star Games has Jean Segura been named to?

a. 0

b. 1

c. 2

d. 3

20. Fernando Vina won two Gold Glove Awards during his 12-season MLB career.

a. True

b. False

QUIZ ANSWERS

1. C – 4

2. A – True

3. B – 4

4. C – 2

5. D – 8

6. C – 3

7. A – True

8. D – 11

9. B – 6

10. C – 3

11. C – 6

12. A – True

13. D – Oakland A's

14. C – 5

15. D – 4

16. B – False (He came in ninth place.)

17. C – 2

18. B – 3

19. C – 2

20. A – True

DID YOU KNOW?

1. Paul Molitor spent 15 seasons of his MLB career with the Milwaukee Brewers. He also played for the Minnesota Twins and Toronto Blue Jays. He is a member of the National Baseball Hall of Fame, seven-time All-Star, four-time Silver Slugger Award winner, World Series champion, the 1993 World Series MVP, and 2017 AL Manager of the Year.

2. Cecil Cooper spent 11 seasons of his MLB career with the Milwaukee Brewers. He also played for the Boston Red Sox. He is a five-time All-Star, three-time Silver Slugger Award winner, and two-time Gold Glove Award winner.

3. Don Money spent 11 seasons of his MLB career with the Milwaukee Brewers. He also played for the Philadelphia Phillies. He is a four-time All-Star.

4. Jeff Cirillo spent eight seasons of his MLB career with the Milwaukee Brewers. He also played for the Colorado Rockies, Seattle Mariners, Arizona Diamondbacks, Minnesota Twins, and San Diego Padres. He is a two-time All-Star.

5. Prince Fielder spent seven seasons of his MLB career with the Milwaukee Brewers. He also played for the Detroit Tigers and Texas Rangers. He is a six-time MLB All-Star, the 2011 All-Star Game MVP, and a three-time Silver Slugger Award winner.

6. Sal Bando spent five seasons of his MLB career with the Milwaukee Brewers. He also played for the Oakland A's. He is a four-time All-Star and three-time World Series champion. He also had a stint as the Brewers' general manager.

7. George Scott spent five seasons of his MLB career with the Milwaukee Brewers. He also played for the Boston Red Sox, Kansas City Royals, and New York Yankees. He is a three-time All-Star and eight-time Gold Glove Award winner.

8. Rickie Weeks spent 11 seasons of his MLB career with the Milwaukee Brewers. He also played for the Arizona Diamondbacks, Tampa Bay Rays, and Seattle Mariners. He was named an All-Star in 2011.

9. Craig Counsell spent six seasons of his MLB career with the Milwaukee Brewers. He also played for the Arizona Diamondbacks, Florida Marlins, Colorado Rockies, and Los Angeles Dodgers. He is a two-time World Series champion and the 2001 NLCS MVP. He is the current manager of the Milwaukee Brewers.

10. Willie Randolph spent a single season of his MLB career with the Milwaukee Brewers. He also played for the New York Yankees, Los Angeles Dodgers, New York Mets, Pittsburgh Pirates, and Oakland A's. He is a six-time All-Star, 1980 Silver Slugger Award winner, and World Series champion.

CHAPTER 12:

PITCHERS & CATCHERS

QUIZ TIME!

1. How many All-Star Games has Jonathan Lucroy been named to in his career?

    a. 0

    b. 1

    c. 2

    d. 3

2. Teddy Higuera spent his entire nine-season MLB career with the Milwaukee Brewers.

    a. True

    b. False

3. How many All-Star Games was Ben Sheets named to during his 10-season MLB career?

    a. 1

    b. 2

    c. 3

    d. 4

4. Chris Bosio spent seven seasons of his MLB career with the Brewers and four seasons with which other franchise?

   a. Texas Rangers

   b. Seattle Mariners

   c. Cleveland Indians

   d. Cincinnati Reds

5. How many Silver Slugger Awards did Yovani Gallardo win during his 12-season MLB career?

   a. 0

   b. 1

   c. 2

   d. 3

6. How many All-Star Games was Jason Kendall named to during his 15-season MLB career?

   a. 1

   b. 3

   c. 5

   d. 6

7. Bill Wegman spent his entire 11-season MLB career with the Milwaukee Brewers.

   a. True

   b. False

8. How many seasons did Mike Caldwell spend with Milwaukee?

   a. 2

   b. 4

c. 6

d. 8

9. Moose Haas spent 10 seasons with the Milwaukee Brewers and two seasons with which other team?

    a. Pittsburgh Pirates

    b. Oakland A's

    c. Kansas City Royals

    d. Texas Rangers

10. What year was Rollie Fingers inducted into the National Baseball Hall of Fame?

    a. 1990

    b. 1991

    c. 1992

    d. 1993

11. How many Cy Young Awards did Pete Vuckovich win during his 11-season MLB career?

    a. 0

    b. 1

    c. 2

    d. 3

12. C.C. Sabathia spent part of one season with the Milwaukee Brewers.

    a. True

    b. False

13. How many All-Star Games was Dan Plesac named to during his 18-season MLB career?

    a. 2

    b. 3

    c. 5

    d. 6

14. John Axford was named the National League Rolaids Relief Pitcher of the Year in which year?

    a. 2009

    b. 2010

    c. 2011

    d. 2012

15. How many All-Star Games was Dan Plesac named to during his 18-season MLB career?

    a. 1

    b. 2

    c. 3

    d. 4

16. Jim Slaton spent 12 seasons of his MLB career with the Milwaukee Brewers.

    a. True

    b. False

17. How many All-Star Games was Chris Capuano named to during his 12-season MLB career?

    a. 0

    b. 1

c. 2

d. 3

18. How many pitching titles has Zack Greinke won?

    a. 0

    b. 1

    c. 2

    d. 3

19. How many seasons did Darrell Porter spend with the Milwaukee Brewers?

    a. 3

    b. 4

    c. 5

    d. 6

20. Don Sutton was inducted into the National Baseball Hall of Fame in 1998.

    a. True

    b. False

QUIZ ANSWERS

1. C – 2

2. A – True

3. D – 4

4. B – Seattle Mariners

5. B – 1

6. B – 3

7. A – True

8. D – 8

9. B – Oakland A's

10. C – 1992

11. B – 1

12. A – True

13. B – 3

14. C – 2011

15. C – 3

16. A – True

17. B – 1

18. C – 2

19. D – 6

20. A – True

DID YOU KNOW?

1. Teddy Higuera spent his entire nine-season MLB career with the Milwaukee Brewers. He was an All-Star in 1986.

2. Rollie Fingers spent four seasons of his MLB career with the Milwaukee Brewers. He also played for the Oakland A's and San Diego Padres. He is a member of the National Baseball Hall of Fame, the 1981 AL MVP, 1981 AL Cy Young Award winner, a seven-time All-Star, three-time World Series champion, the 1974 World Series MVP, and a four-time Rolaids Relief Pitcher of the Year.

3. Ben Sheets spent eight seasons of his MLB career with the Milwaukee Brewers. He also played for the Oakland A's and Atlanta Braves. He is a four-time All-Star.

4. Don Sutton spent three seasons of his MLB career with the Milwaukee Brewers. He also played for the Los Angeles Dodgers, California Angels, Houston Astros, and Oakland A's. He is a member of the National Baseball Hall of Fame, four-time All-Star, 1980 NL leader in ERA, and 1977 All-Star Game MVP.

5. Yovani Gallardo spent eight seasons of his MLB career with the Milwaukee Brewers. He also played for the Texas Rangers, Cincinnati Reds, Seattle Mariners, and Baltimore Orioles. He is a 2010 All-Star and 2010 Silver Slugger Award winner.

6. Jim Slaton spent 12 seasons of his MLB career with the Milwaukee Brewers. He also played for the California Angels and Detroit Tigers. He is a 1977 All-Star.

7. Dan Plesac spent seven seasons of his MLB career with the Milwaukee Brewers. He also played for the Toronto Blue Jays, Arizona Diamondbacks, Pittsburgh Pirates, Philadelphia Phillies, and Chicago Cubs. He is a three-time All-Star.

8. C.C. Sabathia spent less than a season of his MLB career with the Milwaukee Brewers. He also played for the Cleveland Indians and New York Yankees. He is the 2007 AL Cy Young Award winner, a six-time All-Star, World Series champion, and the 2009 ALCS MVP.

9. Zack Greinke spent two seasons of his MLB career with the Milwaukee Brewers. He currently plays for the Houston Astros. He has also played for the Kansas City Royals, Arizona Diamondbacks, Los Angeles Dodgers, and Los Angeles Angels. He won the Cy Young Award in 2009, is a six-time All-Star, six-time Gold Glove Award winner, two-time Silver Slugger Award winner, and two-time ERA leader.

10. Jason Kendall spent two seasons of his MLB career with the Milwaukee Brewers. He also played for the Pittsburgh Pirates, Oakland A's, Kansas City Royals, and Chicago Cubs. He is a three-time All-Star.

CHAPTER 13:

WORLD SERIES

QUIZ TIME!

1. How many World Series championships have the Milwaukee Brewers won in franchise history?

    a. 0

    b. 1

    c. 2

    d. 3

2. How many NL pennants have the Brewers won?

    a. 0

    b. 1

    c. 2

    d. 3

3. How many AL pennants has Milwaukee won?

    a. 0

    b. 1

    c. 2

    d. 3

4. Which team did the Brewers face in the 1982 World Series?

   a. Cincinnati Reds
   b. San Diego Padres
   c. Chicago Cubs
   d. St. Louis Cardinals

5. How many games did the 1982 World Series go?

   a. 4
   b. 5
   c. 6
   d. 7

6. Who was the Brewers' starting pitcher in Game 1 of the 1982 World Series?

   a. Don Sutton
   b. Pete Vuckovich
   c. Mike Caldwell
   d. Jim Slaton

7. The 1982 World Series took place from October 12 to October 20.

   a. True
   b. False

8. Which Milwaukee batter hit the most home runs in the 1982 World Series?

   a. Cecil Cooper
   b. Ted Simmons

97

c. Robin Yount

d. Ben Oglivie

9. Which Brewers batter had the most RBIs in the 1982 World Series?

a. Robin Yount

b. Cecil Cooper

c. Jim Gantner

d. Both A and B

10. Which Milwaukee batter had the most at-bats in the 1982 World Series?

a. Robin Yount

b. Cecil Cooper

c. Paul Molitor

d. Gorman Thomas

11. Which Brewers pitcher had the most wins in the 1982 World Series?

a. Mike Caldwell

b. Jim Slaton

c. Moose Haas

d. Don Sutton

12. Of all the Brewers' pitchers, Don Sutton allowed the most earned runs during the 1982 World Series, with nine.

a. True

b. False

13. Which Milwaukee pitcher recorded the most strikeouts in the 1982 World Series?

    a. Pete Vuckovich
    b. Don Sutton
    c. Bob McClure
    d. Mike Caldwell

14. Which Brewers pitcher gave up the most walks in the 1982 World Series?

    a. Bob McClure
    b. Moose Haas
    c. Pete Vuckovich
    d. Doc Medich

15. Which Milwaukee pitcher pitched the most innings in the 1982 World Series?

    a. Pete Vuckovich
    b. Don Sutton
    c. Mike Caldwell
    d. Moose Haas

16. The Brewers faced the California Angels in the 1982 American League Championship Series.

    a. True
    b. False

17. Who was the Brewers' manager during the 1982 World Series?

    a. George Bamberger
    b. Rene Lachemann

c. Buck Rodgers

d. Harvey Kuenn

18. Which Milwaukee batter had the best batting average in the 1982 World Series?

    a. Charlie Moore

    b. Jim Gantner

    c. Paul Molitor

    d. Robin Yount

19. Which Brewers batter was walked the most in the 1982 World Series?

    a. Ben Oglivie

    b. Ted Simmons

    c. Gorman Thomas

    d. Ned Yost

20. Bob McClure had the most losses of Milwaukee's pitchers in the 1982 World Series, with two.

    a. True

    b. False

QUIZ ANSWERS

1. A – 0

2. A – 0

3. B – 1

4. D – St. Louis Cardinals

5. D – 7

6. C – Mike Caldwell

7. A – True

8. B – Ted Simmons (2)

9. D – Both A and B (Yount and Cooper recorded six RBIs each.)

10. C – Paul Molitor (31)

11. A – Mike Caldwell (2)

12. A – True

13. D – Mike Caldwell (6)

14. C – Pete Vuckovich (5)

15. C – Mike Caldwell (17.2 IP)

16. A – True

17. D – Harvey Kuenn

18. D – Robin Yount (.414)

19. B – Ted Simmons (5)

20. A – True

DID YOU KNOW?

1. Darrell Porter was named the 1982 World Series MVP.

2. Bob McClure had the most saves of Milwaukee's pitchers in the 1982 World Series, with two.

3. Mike Caldwell threw a complete game in Game 1 of the 1982 World Series.

4. Robin Yount had the most hits of Milwaukee's batters in the 1982 World Series, with 12.

5. Cecil Cooper, Jim Gantner, Paul Molitor, Charlie Moore, Ben Oglivie, Ted Simmons, Gorman Thomas, and Robin Yount played in all seven games of the 1982 World Series.

6. Rollie Fingers missed the 1982 World Series with the Brewers due to a muscle tear in his arm.

7. Since Milwaukee and St. Louis are known for their beer, the 1982 World Series earned the nickname "The Suds Series."

8. Games 1 and 2 of the 1982 World Series took place at Busch Stadium. Games 3, 4, and 5 took place at County Stadium. Games 6 and 7 took place back at Busch Stadium.

9. Game 1 of the 1982 World Series was the Brewers' last postseason road game win until October 13, 2011, which was coincidentally also against the Cardinals.

10. Paul Molitor set a World Series record in 1982 for having five hits in Game 1.

CHAPTER 14:

HEATED RIVALRIES

QUIZ TIME!

1. Which team does NOT play in the National League Central with the Milwaukee Brewers?

   a. Pittsburgh Pirates
   b. Chicago Cubs
   c. Cincinnati Reds
   d. Detroit Tigers

2. The Brewers were a part of the American League West Division from 1969 to 1971.

   a. True
   b. False

3. Which team below was once a member of the NL Central Division?

   a. Philadelphia Phillies
   b. Houston Astros
   c. Chicago White Sox
   d. Minnesota Twins

4. What current National League Central team has the most NL Central championships?

    a. Milwaukee Brewers
    b. Chicago Cubs
    c. Cincinnati Reds
    d. St. Louis Cardinals

5. From 1998 to 2013, the NL Central was the MLB's largest division.

    a. True
    b. False

6. Which team won the National League Central in 2020?

    a. St. Louis Cardinals
    b. Chicago Cubs
    c. Cincinnati Reds
    d. Detroit Tigers

7. The Pittsburgh Pirates have never won a NL Central division championship.

    a. True
    b. False

8. The Milwaukee Brewers have not won a World Series championship. How many have the St. Louis Cardinals won?

    a. 5
    b. 6
    c. 11
    d. 12

9. The Milwaukee Brewers have not won a World Series championship. How many have the Chicago Cubs won?

   a. 0
   b. 1
   c. 2
   d. 3

10. The Milwaukee Brewers have not won a World Series championship. How many have the Cincinnati Reds won?

    a. 1
    b. 2
    c. 5
    d. 6

11. The Milwaukee Brewers have not won a World Series championship. How many have the Pittsburgh Pirates won?

    a. 0
    b. 1
    c. 3
    d. 5

12. The Milwaukee Brewers were members of the American League East Division from 1972 to 1993.

    a. True
    b. False

13. Which player has NOT played for both the Milwaukee Brewers and the St. Louis Cardinals?

a. Mike Matheny

b. Kyle Lohse

c. John Axford

d. Corey Hart

14. Which player has NOT played for both the Milwaukee Brewers and the Pittsburgh Pirates?

   a. Jason Kendall

   b. Tom Brunansky

   c. Dave Parker

   d. Neil Walker

15. Which player has NOT played for both the Milwaukee Brewers and the Cincinnati Reds?

   a. Mike Caldwell

   b. Mike Moustakas

   c. Gorman Thomas

   d. Kyle Lohse

16. The Milwaukee Brewers were members of the American League Central Division from 1994 to 1997.

   a. True

   b. False

17. Which player has NOT played for both the Milwaukee Brewers and the Chicago Cubs?

   a. Jeromy Burnitz

   b. Jonathan Lucroy

   c. Dan Plesac

   d. Geoff Jenkins

18. Which player has NOT played for both the Milwaukee Brewers and the Houston Astros?

    a. Chris Carter
    b. Yovani Gallardo
    c. Zack Greinke
    d. Pat Listach

19. How many NL Central division titles did the Houston Astros win before they moved to the AL West?

    a. 0
    b. 1
    c. 3
    d. 4

20. The Brewers won two AL East division championships before they moved to the NL Central.

    a. True
    b. False

QUIZ ANSWERS

1. D – Detroit Tigers

2. A – True

3. B – Houston Astros

4. D – St. Louis Cardinals (11)

5. A – True

6. B – Chicago Cubs

7. A – True

8. C – 11

9. D – 3

10. C – 5

11. D – 5

12. A – True

13. D – Corey Hart

14. B – Tom Brunansky

15. C – Gorman Thomas

16. A – True

17. D – Geoff Jenkins

18. B – Yovani Gallardo

19. D – 4

20. A – True

DID YOU KNOW?

1. The St. Louis Cardinals have the most National League Central division championships, with 11. The Chicago Cubs have six, the Cincinnati Reds have three, and the Milwaukee Brewers have two. The Pittsburgh Pirates have not won an NL Central division championship so far in their history. The Houston Astros, currently playing in the AL West Division, won four division championships during their time in the NL Central. The Milwaukee Brewers won their two NL Central titles in 2011 and 2018. During their time in the AL East Division, they also won two division titles.

2. When the NL Central was founded, the Pirates were originally supposed to stay in the NL East, with the Atlanta Braves set to move to the NL Central from the NL West. The Braves requested to stay in the East Division due to their rivalry with the Florida Marlins. The Pirates have requested to be placed back in the East Division several times.

3. The Chicago Cubs, Cincinnati Reds, St. Louis Cardinals, Houston Astros, and Pittsburgh Pirates are all founding members of the National League Central Division.

4. The first NL Central division champions were the Cincinnati Reds in 1995. There were no playoffs in 1994 due to the MLB strike.

5. The Milwaukee Brewers are the only team in the National League Central that has not won a World Series championship.

6. John Axford, David Bell, Jonathan Broxton, Tom Brunansky, Jose Cardenal, Jim Edmonds, Tito Francona, Jedd Gyorko, Brian Harper, Cesar Izturis, Marcus Jensen, George Kottaras, Ted Kubiak, Sixto Lezcano, Kyle Lohse, Felipe Lopez, Mike Matheny, Bob McClure, Tom Murphy, Chris Narveson, Darrell Porter, Alberto Reyes, Mark Reynolds, Dick Schofield, Ted Simmons, Carlos Villanueva, Ron Villone, Fernando Vina, Pete Vuckovich, Kolten Wong, and Jamey Wright have played for both the Milwaukee Brewers and the St. Louis Cardinals.

7. Brett Anderson, Steve Barber, Quentin Berry, Henry Blanco, Jeromy Burnitz, Jose Cardenal, Jim Colborn, Chuck Crim, Zach Davies, Doug Davis, Jim Edmonds, Terry Francona, Rob Gardner, Matt Garza, Jerry Hairston, LaTroy Hawkins, Jose Hernandez, Tyler Houston, Cesar Izturis, Jeremy Jeffress, Doug Jones, Jason Kendall, Brandon Kintzler, Jonathan Lucroy, Martin Maldonado, Casey McGehee, Dan Plesac, Aramis Ramirez, Bob Scanlan, Eric Sogard, Matt Stairs, Jim Sundberg, David Weathers, and Eric Young Sr. have played for both the Milwaukee Brewers and the Chicago Cubs.

8. Rick Auerbach, Russell Branyan, Jonathan Broxton, Mike Caldwell, Mike Cameron, Bernie Carbo, Francisco Cordero, Bill Doran, Jim Edmonds, Terry Francona, Yovani Gallardo,

Scooter Gennett, Jerry Hairston, Jeffrey Hammonds, Tommy Harper, Paul Householder, Cesar Izturis, Tim Leary, Kyle Lohse, Felipe Lopez, Wade Miley, Mike Moustakas, Joe Oliver, Dave Parker, Ted Savage, John Vander Wal, Greg Vaughn, John Vukovich, and David Weathers have played for both the Milwaukee Brewers and the Cincinnati Reds.

9. John Axford, Chris Duffy, Brian Harper, Jason Kendall, Casey McGehee, Nyjer Morgan, Lyle Overbay, Dave Parker, Dan Plesac, Aramis Ramirez, Dick Schofield, Joakim Soria, Matt Stairs, Dale Sveum, John Vander Wal, and Neil Walker have played for both the Milwaukee Brewers and the Pittsburgh Pirates.

10. Nori Aoki, Chuck Carr, Chris Carter, Francisco Cordero, Bill Doran, Mike Felder, Keith Ginter, Carlos Gomez, Zack Greinke, Bill Hall, LaTroy Hawkins, Doug Henry, Paul Householder, Pete Ladd, Carlos Lee, Pat Listach, Mark Loretta, Martin Maldonado, Wade Miley, Bill Spiers, Franklin Stubbs, Don Sutton, and Jonathan Villar have played for both the Milwaukee Brewers and the Houston Astros.

CHAPTER 15:

THE AWARDS SECTION

QUIZ TIME!

1. Which Milwaukee Brewers player won the American League MVP Award in 1981?

   a. Cecil Cooper

   b. Rollie Fingers

   c. Robin Yount

   d. Sal Bando

2. Bob Uecker won the Ford C. Frick Award in 2003.

   a. True

   b. False

3. How many Gold Glove Awards did George Scott win during his time with the Brewers?

   a. 1

   b. 3

   c. 4

   d. 5

4. Who is the only Milwaukee player to ever win the Roberto Clemente Award?

   a. Paul Molitor
   b. Robin Yount
   c. Cecil Cooper
   d. Prince Fielder

5. Who are the only two Brewers pitchers to ever win the Cy Young Award?

   a. Rollie Fingers and Yovani Gallardo
   b. Rollie Fingers and Pete Vuckovich
   c. Pete Vuckovich and Teddy Higuera
   d. Chris Bosio and Moose Haas

6. Which Milwaukee player won a Silver Slugger Award in 2018?

   a. Lorenzo Cain
   b. Ryan Braun
   c. Christian Yelich
   d. Both A and B

7. No Milwaukee Brewers player has ever won the MLB Home Run Derby.

   a. True
   b. False

8. Which Brewers player was named the DHL Hometown Hero? (Voted by MLB fans as the most outstanding player in franchise history.)

a. Paul Molitor

b. Robin Yount

c. Cecil Cooper

d. Rollie Fingers

9. Who was the first Milwaukee player to win a Gold Glove Award?

a. Sixto Lezcano

b. Cecil Cooper

c. George Scott

d. Robin Yount

10. Who was the first Brewers player to win a Silver Slugger Award?

a. Dave Parker

b. Robin Yount

c. Ben Oglivie

d. Cecil Cooper

11. Which Milwaukee player won the 2019 Wilson Defensive Player of the Year Award?

a. Lorenzo Cain

b. Mike Moustakas

c. Christian Yelich

d. Ryan Bruan

12. Prince Fielder is the only Milwaukee player to win the MLB All-Star Game MVP Award.

a. True

b. False

13. Which two pitchers are the only Brewers to ever win the Rolaids Relief Man of the Year Award?

    a. Rollie Fingers and Dan Plesac
    b. Rollie Fingers and John Axford
    c. Trevor Hoffman and John Axford
    d. Trevor Hoffman and Dan Plesac

14. Which Milwaukee player won the 2020 National League Rookie of the Year Award?

    a. Adrian Houser
    b. Bobby Wahl
    c. Corbin Burnes
    d. Devin Williams

15. Who was the first Brewers player to win the Rookie of the Year Award?

    a. Prince Fielder
    b. Robin Yount
    c. Pat Listach
    d. Ryan Braun

16. No Milwaukee Brewers manager has ever won the Manager of the Year Award.

    a. True
    b. False

17. Who is the only Brewers pitcher to win a Silver Slugger Award?

    a. Ben Sheets
    b. Mike Caldwell

   c. Sixto Lezcano

   d. Yovani Gallardo

18. Who are the only two Milwaukee players to win a Hank Aaron Award?

   a. Prince Fielder and Christian Yelich

   b. Prince Fielder and Ryan Braun

   c. Ryan Braun and Christian Yelich

   d. Christian Yelich and Lorenzo Cain

19. Who is the only Brewers player to win an Edgar Martinez Award?

   a. Prince Fielder

   b. Dave Parker

   c. Jonathan Lucroy

   d. Yovani Gallardo

20. Christian Yelich was named the 2018 National League MVP.

   a. True

   b. False

QUIZ ANSWERS

1. B – Rollie Fingers

2. A – True

3. D – 5

4. C – Cecil Cooper

5. B – Rollie Fingers and Pete Vuckovich

6. C – Christian Yelich

7. B – False (Prince Fielder won the Home Run Derby in 2009.)

8. B – Robin Yount

9. C – George Scott (1972)

10. D – Cecil Cooper (1980)

11. A – Lorenzo Cain

12. A – True (Fielder won the award in 2011.)

13. B – Rollie Fingers and John Axford

14. D – Devin Williams

15. C – Pat Listach (1992)

16. A – True

17. D – Yovani Gallardo (2010)

18. A – Prince Fielder and Christian Yelich (Yelich has two.)

19. B – Dave Parker (1990)

20. A – True

DID YOU KNOW?

1. The Milwaukee Brewers have had two different players win Cy Young Awards in franchise history: Rollie Fingers (1981) and Pete Vuckovich (1982).

2. The Brewers have had 10 different players win Silver Slugger Awards in franchise history: Cecil Cooper, Ben Oglivie, Robin Yount, Paul Molitor, Dave Parker, Carlos Lee, Prince Fielder, Ryan Braun, Yovani Gallardo, and Christian Yelich.

3. Milwaukee has had three players named Rookie of the Year in franchise history: Pat Listach (1992), Ryan Braun (2007), and Devin Williams (2020).

4. The Brewers have had six different players win Gold Glove Awards in franchise history: George Scott, Cecil Cooper, Sixto Lezcano, Robin Yount, Carlos Gomez, and Lorenzo Cain.

5. Milwaukee has had four different players win an MVP award in franchise history: Rollie Fingers (1981), Robin Yount (1982 and 1989), Ryan Braun (2011), and Christian Yelich (2018).

6. The Brewers have had two different players win the Wilson Defensive Player of the Year Award in franchise history: Carlos Gomez (2012 and 2013) and Lorenzo Cain (2019).

7. Milwaukee has had only two players win the Trevor Hoffman Award in franchise history: Josh Hader in 2018 and 2019, then Devin Williams in 2020.

8. Five Brewers players have won the MLB Pitcher of the Month Award: Cal Eldred (2), Jeff D'Amico, Ben Sheets, C.C. Sabathia (2), and Trevor Hoffman.

9. Six Milwaukee players have won the MLB Rookie of the Month Award: Ben Sheets, Scott Podsednik, Prince Fielder, Ryan Braun (2), Casey McGehee, and Keston Hiura.

10. Eight Brewers players have won the MLB Player of the Month Award: Robin Yount (3), Cecil Cooper (4), Ben Oglivie, Paul Molitor, Jeromy Burnitz, Prince Fielder (2), Ryan Braun (4), and Christian Yelich.

CHAPTER 16:

CREAM CITY

QUIZ TIME!

1. The Milwaukee Public Museum is home to the world's largest of which artifact?

    a. Bronze statue
    b. Native American totem pole
    c. Mummy tomb
    d. Dinosaur skull

2. There is a bronze statue of Fonzie from *Happy Days* on the Milwaukee RiverWalk.

    a. True
    b. False

3. Which celebrity was NOT born in Milwaukee?

    a. Gene Wilder
    b. Beyoncé
    c. Colin Kaepernick
    d. Alfred Lunt

4. Which of the following was invented in Milwaukee?

    a. Vaccuum
    b. Steam engine
    c. Typewriter
    d. Television

5. Which Milwaukee downtown structure is bigger than Times Square?

    a. Ice rink
    b. Zoo
    c. Riverfront
    d. Bird sanctuary

6. Which lip balm company got its start in Milwaukee?

    a. Blistex
    b. Chapstick
    c. Carmex
    d. EOS

7. Between 50 and 60 cream puffs are sold per minute at the Wisconsin State Fair.

    a. True
    b. False

8. What is the name of Wisconsin's NFL team?

    a. Milwaukee Raiders
    b. Green Bay Packers
    c. Green Bay 49ers
    d. Milwaukee Cowboys

9. What is the name of Milwaukee's NBA team?

    a. Milwaukee Pistons

    b. Milwaukee Kings

    c. Milwaukee Warriors

    d. Milwaukee Bucks

10. How many Super Bowls have the Green Bay Packers won?

    a. 2

    b. 4

    c. 6

    d. 8

11. What is the name of the Green Bay Packers' current stadium?

    a. Lambeau Field

    b. Heinz Field

    c. Arrowhead Stadium

    d. State Farm Stadium

12. The Milwaukee Bucks currently have one NBA championship.

    a. True

    b. False

13. What is the name of the Milwaukee Bucks' current arena?

    a. Staples Center

    b. Smoothie King Center

    c. Fiserv Forum

    d. Chase Center

14. The Atlanta Braves were once based in Milwaukee and known as the Milwaukee Braves.

    a. True
    b. False

15. Which TV sitcom was set in Milwaukee?

    a. *I Love Lucy*
    b. *Laverne & Shirley*
    c. *King of Queens*
    d. *Modern Family*

16. The answering machine was invented in Milwaukee.

    a. True
    b. False

17. Which of the following was Milwaukee's first brewery?

    a. Point Brewery
    b. Miller Brewing Company
    c. Potosi Brewing Company
    d. Pabst Brewery

18. What is Milwaukee Mitchell International Airport's IATA code?

    a. MMI
    b. MKE
    c. MMA
    d. MKI

19. The oldest type of what building in the United States is in Milwaukee?

a. Zoo
b. Ice skating rink
c. Bowling alley
d. McDonald's restaurant

20. President Teddy Roosevelt was shot during an assassination attempt in Milwaukee in 1916.

    a. True
    b. False

QUIZ ANSWERS

1. D – Dinosaur skull

2. A – True

3. B – Beyoncé

4. C – Typewriter

5. A – Ice rink

6. C – Carmex

7. A – True

8. B – Green Bay Packers

9. D – Milwaukee Bucks

10. B – 4

11. A – Lambeau Field

12. A – True

13. C – Fiserv Forum

14. A – True

15. B – *Laverne & Shirley*

16. A – True

17. D – Pabst Brewery

18. B – MKE

19. C – Bowling alley

20. A – True (He was saved by the glasses case in his pocket. He finished his speech before receiving care.)

DID YOU KNOW?

1. Milwaukee is the largest city in Wisconsin.

2. Milwaukee is home to Summerfest, the world's largest music festival. Who needs Coachella?

3. The Harley-Davidson Motor Company was created in Milwaukee, which is also home to the world's only Harley-Davidson museum.

4. Since 1960, the city of Milwaukee has had only four mayors. One of those mayors only served for three months in the position.

5. The Milwaukee Art Museum building has wings called the Burke Brise Soleil. It is a sun screen that sits atop the glass hall. They open each morning and close at night. They will automatically close if the wind goes above 23 miles per hour.

6. In the nineteenth century, major industries in Milwaukee included milling flour and iron founding.

7. Beer production in Milwaukee began in 1840.

8. The city zoo is called the Milwaukee County Zoo, and it is home to over 2,200 animals.

9. The Milwaukee Wave is the oldest continually operating soccer team in the United States.

10. The iconic TV show, *Happy Days*, was set in Milwaukee, Wisconsin, just like *Laverne & Shirley*.

CHAPTER 17:

COOP

QUIZ TIME!

1. What is Willie Cecil Cooper's full name?

   a. Christopher Cecil Cooper

   b. Cecil Christopher Cooper

   c. Cecil Celester Cooper

   d. Celester Cecil Cooper

2. Cecil Cooper played his entire 17-season MLB career with the Milwaukee Brewers.

   a. True

   b. False

3. Where was Cecil Cooper born?

   a. Brenham, Texas

   b. Prairie View, Texas

   c. Laredo, Texas

   d. Denton, Texas

4. When was Cecil Cooper born?

a. June 20, 1940

b. June 20, 1949

c. December 20, 1940

d. December 20, 1949

5. Cecil Cooper won the 1983 Roberto Clemente Award.

   a. True

   b. False

6. How many Gold Glove Awards did Cecil Cooper win during his MLB career?

   a. 0

   b. 1

   c. 2

   d. 3

7. Cecil Cooper was manager of which MLB team from 2007 to 2009?

   a. Boston Red Sox

   b. Los Angeles Angels

   c. Milwaukee Brewers

   d. Houston Astros

8. Cecil Cooper is a member of the National Baseball Hall of Fame.

   a. True

   b. False

9. How many World Series championships did Cecil Cooper win during his MLB career?

a. 0

b. 1

c. 2

d. 3

10. What year did Cecil Cooper make his MLB debut?

a. 1970

b. 1971

c. 1973

d. 1975

11. How many All-Star Games was Cecil Cooper named to during his MLB career?

a. 1

b. 3

c. 4

d. 5

12. Cecil Cooper's uniform number 15 is retired by the Milwaukee Brewers.

a. True

b. False

13. How many times did Cecil Cooper lead the American League in RBIs during his MLB career?

a. 1

b. 2

c. 3

d. 4

14. Cecil Cooper is a member of the American Family Field Walk of Fame.

   a. True
   b. False

15. How many Silver Slugger Awards did Cecil Cooper win during his MLB career?

   a. 1
   b. 2
   c. 3
   d. 4

16. How many times was Cecil Cooper named the AL Player of the Month during his MLB career?

   a. 1
   b. 2
   c. 3
   d. 4

17. Cecil Cooper was named the AL Player of the Week five times during his MLB career.

   a. True
   b. False

18. How many home runs did Cecil Cooper hit during his MLB career?

   a. 211
   b. 221
   c. 241
   d. 251

19. How many RBIs did Cecil Cooper collect during his MLB career?

    a. 1,025

    b. 1,125

    c. 1,225

    d. 1,425

20. Cecil Cooper's career batting average is .298.

    a. True

    b. False

QUIZ ANSWERS

1. C – Cecil Celester Cooper

2. B – False (He played for the Brewers and Boston Red Sox.)

3. A – Brenham, Texas

4. D – December 20, 1949

5. A – True

6. C – 2

7. D – Houston Astros

8. B – False

9. A – 0

10. B – 1971

11. D – 5

12. B – False

13. B – 2 (1980, 1983)

14. A – True

15. C – 3 (1980, 1981, 1982)

16. D – 4 (April 1979, August 1980, August 1981, July 1983)

17. A – True

18. C – 241

19. B – 1,125

20. A – True

DID YOU KNOW?

1. Cecil Cooper stole 89 bases during his 17-season MLB career.

2. Over the course of his MLB career, Cecil Cooper had a total of 7,349 at-bats.

3. Cecil Cooper collected 2,192 hits during his MLB career.

4. Cecil Cooper's career WAR value is 36.0.

5. Cecil Cooper attended college at Prairie View A&M University in Texas.

6. In 2007, Cecil Cooper was elected into the Wisconsin Athletic Hall of Fame.

7. In 2002, Cecil Cooper was bench coach for the Milwaukee Brewers. After one year in that position, he managed the Indianapolis Indians until 2004. Then, in 2005, the Houston Astros hired him as bench coach. And, in 2007, Cooper made Astros history by becoming the franchise's first African-American manager.

8. Cecil Cooper spent 11 seasons of his career with the Milwaukee Brewers and six seasons of his career with the Boston Red Sox.

9. In 1971, at the age of 21, Cecil Cooper made his MLB debut. He played in his final MLB game in 1987 at the age of 37.

10. Cecil Cooper currently lives in Texas with his wife Octavia. He has three daughters: Tori, Brittany, and Kelly.

CHAPTER 18:

HAMMERIN' HANK

QUIZ TIME!

1. Where was Hank Aaron born?

    a. Savannah, Georgia

    b. Montgomery, Alabama

    c. Mobile, Alabama

    d. Atlanta, Georgia

2. Hank Aaron spent his entire 23-season MLB career with the Milwaukee Brewers.

    a. True

    b. False

3. What year was Hank Aaron inducted into the National Baseball Hall of Fame with 97.8% of the first ballot vote?

    a. 1980

    b. 1982

    c. 1985

    d. 1989

4. Hank Aaron holds the record for most RBIs in MLB history. How many did he collect during his MLB career?

    a. 1,997
    b. 2,097
    c. 2,197
    d. 2,297

5. What year was Hank Aaron born?

    a. 1930
    b. 1932
    c. 1934
    d. 1936

6. How many times was Hank Aaron named the NL MVP during his MLB career?

    a. 1
    b. 3
    c. 4
    d. 6

7. Hank Aaron won two NL batting titles during his MLB career.

    a. True
    b. False

8. How many World Series championships did Hank Aaron win during his MLB career?

    a. 0
    b. 1

c. 3

d. 5

9. How many Gold Glove Awards did Hank Aaron win during his MLB career?

    a. 1

    b. 3

    c. 6

    d. 7

10. How many All-Star Games was Hank Aaron named to during his MLB career?

    a. 18

    b. 20

    c. 23

    d. 25

11. What year did the Milwaukee Brewers retire Hank Aaron's uniform number 44?

    a. 1976

    b. 1977

    c. 1978

    d. 1979

12. Hank Aaron hit 24 or more home runs every single season from 1955 to 1973.

    a. True

    b. False

13. Hank Aaron was awarded the Presidential Medal of Freedom by which US President?

    a. Jimmy Carter
    b. Bill Clinton
    c. George W. Bush
    d. Barack Obama

14. What year was Hank Aaron inducted into the Wisconsin Athletic Hall of Fame?

    a. 1980
    b. 1988
    c. 1993
    d. 1995

15. Hank Aaron was a longtime fan of which NFL team?

    a. San Francisco 49ers
    b. Atlanta Falcons
    c. Green Bay Packers
    d. Cleveland Browns

16. Hank Aaron completed a total of 12,364 at-bats during his MLB career.

    a. True
    b. False

17. How many home runs did Hank Aaron hit during his MLB career?

    a. 744
    b. 755

c. 766

d. 788

18. What is Hank Aaron's career batting average?

    a. .295

    b. .300

    c. .305

    d. .315

19. How many stolen bases did Hank Aaron collect during his MLB career?

    a. 210

    b. 220

    c. 230

    d. 240

20. Hank Aaron's career WAR value is 143.1.

    a. True

    b. False

QUIZ ANSWERS

1. C – Mobile, Alabama
2. B – False (He played for the Milwaukee/Atlanta Braves for 21 years and the Brewers for two years.)
3. B – 1982
4. D – 2,297
5. C – 1934
6. A – 1 (1957)
7. A – True (Aaron won the batting titles in 1956 and 1959.)
8. B – 1 (1957)
9. B – 3
10. D – 25 (There were two All-Star Games in 1961 and 1962.)
11. A – 1976
12. A – True
13. C – George W. Bush
14. B – 1988
15. D – Cleveland Browns
16. A – True
17. B – 755
18. C – .305
19. D – 240
20. A – True

DID YOU KNOW?

1. In 1999, the MLB created the Hank Aaron Award. Each year it is given to the best hitter in each league.

2. Hank Aaron was named to the MLB All-Century Team in 1999. Other players named to this team included: Nolan Ryan, Sandy Koufax, Cy Young, Roger Clemens, Bob Gibson, Walter Johnson, Warren Spahn, Christy Mathewson, Lefty Grove, Johnny Bench, Yogi Berra, Lou Gehrig, Mark McGwire, Jackie Robinson, Rogers Hornsby, Mike Schmidt, Brooks Robinson, Cal Ripken Jr., Ernie Banks, Honus Wagner, Babe Ruth, Ted Williams, Willie Mays, Joe DiMaggio, Mickey Mantle, Ty Cobb, Ken Griffey Jr., Pete Rose, and Stan Musial.

3. An Atlanta high school, Forrest Hill Academy, was renamed Hank Aaron New Beginnings Academy in April 2021.

4. On January 8, 2001, Hank Aaron was awarded the Presidential Citizens Medal by President Bill Clinton.

5. Hank Aaron was awarded the 1976 Spingarn Medal from the NAACP.

6. After retiring from baseball, Hank Aaron worked in the Atlanta Braves front office. He spent some time as their senior vice president.

7. Hank Aaron once owned a BMW dealership called Hank Aaron BMW of South Atlanta. Each car sold came with a free Hank Aaron autographed baseball.

8. Hank Aaron's 755 home runs broke Babe Ruth's all-time MLB record for career home runs.

9. Hank Aaron is one of only two players in MLB history to hit 30 or more home runs in a season at least 15 times.

10. Hank Aaron is one of only four players in MLB history to have 150 or more hits in at least 17 seasons.

CHAPTER 19:

AMERICA'S PASTIME

QUIZ TIME!

1. How many total teams play in Major League Baseball?

   a. 15
   b. 20
   c. 30
   d. 33

2. Major League Baseball was founded in 1903.

   a. True
   b. False

3. Who is the current commissioner of Major League Baseball?

   a. Bart Giamatti
   b. Fay Vincent
   c. Bud Selig
   d. Rob Manfred

4. What year was the National League founded?

a. 1870

b. 1876

c. 1903

d. 1911

5. What year was the American League founded?

    a. 1888

    b. 1901

    c. 1903

    d. 1918

6. Major League Baseball is the second wealthiest professional sports league. Which league is the wealthiest?

    a. NBA

    b. NHL

    c. NFL

    d. MLS

7. The Major League Baseball headquarters is located in New York City.

    a. True

    b. False

8. How many games does each Major League Baseball team play per season?

    a. 92

    b. 122

    c. 162

    d. 192

9. In which two US states is Major League Baseball's spring training held?

    a. California and Florida
    b. Arizona and Florida
    c. Arizona and California
    d. California and Arkansas

10. How many stitches does an official MLB baseball have?

    a. 98
    b. 100
    c. 108
    d. 110

11. Where is the National Baseball Hall of Fame located?

    a. Denver, Colorado
    b. Phoenix, Arizona
    c. Los Angeles, California
    d. Cooperstown, New York

12. All 30 Major League Baseball teams are located in the United States.

    a. True
    b. False

13. Which current Major League Baseball stadium is the oldest baseball stadium still in use?

    a. Angel Stadium
    b. Dodger Stadium
    c. Fenway Park
    d. Wrigley Field

14. Major League Baseball has the highest attendance of any sports league in the world.

    a. True
    b. False

15. Fill in the blank: Seventh Inning _____

    a. Jog
    b. Song
    c. Shake
    d. Stretch

16. William Howard Taft was the first United States president to throw out the ceremonial first pitch at a Major League Baseball game.

    a. True
    b. False

17. To follow a Major League Baseball rule, all umpires must wear what color underwear in case they rip their pants?

    a. Tan
    b. Gray
    c. White
    d. Black

18. What year did the first Major League Baseball World Series take place?

    a. 1903
    b. 1905
    c. 1915
    d. 1920

19. Former Major League Baseball Commissioner Bart Giamatti is the father of actor Paul Giamatti.

    a. True
    b. False

20. The song traditionally played in the middle of the 7th inning at Major League Baseball games is called "Take Me Out to the Ballpark."

    a. True
    b. False

QUIZ ANSWERS

1. C – 30

2. A – True

3. D – Rob Manfred

4. B – 1876

5. B – 1901

6. C – NFL

7. A – True

8. C – 162

9. B – Arizona and Florida

10. C – 108

11. D – Cooperstown, New York

12. B – False (The Toronto Blue Jays are located in Canada.)

13. C – Fenway Park

14. A – True

15. D – Stretch

16. A – True

17. D – Black

18. A – 1903

19. A – True

20. B – False ("Take Me Out to the Ball Game")

DID YOU KNOW?

1. The average lifespan of a baseball in a Major League Baseball game is seven pitches. This means approximately 5-6 dozen baseballs are used in every game.

2. The Boston Americans won the very first Major League Baseball World Series. They defeated the Pittsburgh Pirates in eight games. Today, the most games a World Series can go is seven.

3. The New York Yankees currently hold the most World Series titles in Major League Baseball, with 27.

4. Hot dogs are the most popular food item sold at Major League Baseball ballparks. Over 21 million hot dogs were sold at MLB stadiums in 2014.

5. The longest Major League Baseball game on record occurred on May 9, 1984, between the Chicago White Sox and Milwaukee Brewers. The game lasted eight hours and six minutes. The most innings played in a Major League Baseball game was 26 innings on May 1, 1920, between the Brooklyn Dodgers and Boston Braves.

6. The distance from the pitching mound to home plate at Major League Baseball ballparks is 60.5 feet.

7. Before they can be used in a Major League Baseball game, each baseball is rubbed with a special mud to improve

grip and reduce luster. This special mud comes from a specific, secret location in the state of New Jersey.

8. The fastest Major League Baseball game on record took place on September 28, 1919, which was played between the New York Giants and Philadelphia Phillies, and took 51 minutes. An average MLB game is three hours.

9. The American League uses a designated hitter. A DH only hits and does not play in the field. In the National League, the pitcher hits instead of using a designated hitter. If an interleague game is being played, whether a DH is used or not is determined by which team is the home team. If the home team is from the American League, each team will use a DH. If the home team is from the National League, each team's pitcher will hit.

10. The distance between each of the four bases in Major League Baseball is 90 feet.

CONCLUSION

Now you truly are the ultimate Brewers fan! We hope you learned something new about the Brew Crew of the modern era, and that you expanded your knowledge by revisiting the early days of the franchise.

You learned about the Milwaukee Brewers' origins and how far they have come. You learned about the history of their uniforms and jersey numbers and read some of the craziest nicknames of all time. You learned more about the legendary Cecil Cooper and Hall-of-Famers Robin Yount, Paul Molitor, and Hammerin' Hank Aaron. You were amazed by Brewers stats and recalled some of the most infamous Brewers trades and draft picks of all time. You broke down your knowledge by outfielders, infielders, pitchers, and catchers. You looked back on the Brewers' playoff feats and the awards that came before, after, and during them. You also learned about the Brewers' fiercest rivalries both inside and outside of their division.

Every team in the MLB has a storied history, but the Milwaukee Brewers have one of the most memorable of all. They have gone through winning seasons and losing seasons with the backing of their devoted fans. Being the ultimate

Brewers fan takes knowledge and a whole lot of patience, which you tested with this book. Whether you knew every answer or were stumped by several questions, you learned some of the most interesting history that the game of baseball has to offer.

The deep history of the Milwaukee Brewers franchise represents what we all love about the game of baseball. The heart, the determination, the tough times, and the unexpected moments, plus the players that inspire us and encourage us to do our best, because even if you get knocked down, there is always another game and another day.

With players like Christian Yelich, Devin Williams, and Jackie Bradley Jr., the future for the Milwaukee Brewers continues to look bright. They have a lot to prove, but there is no doubt that this franchise will continue to be one of the most competitive teams in Major League Baseball year after year.

It's a new decade, which means there is a clean slate, ready to continue writing the history of the Milwaukee Brewers. The ultimate Brewers fan cannot wait to see what's to come for their beloved Brew Crew.

Made in the USA
Monee, IL
10 September 2024

65500169R10090